Volume One

TEMPEST

Natasha Kennedy

Story and illustration by Natasha Kennedy

Illustrations drawn with Procreate iOS App
Book compiled with Adobe InDesign CC

Page 4: *The Flammarion Engraving*, 1888, artist unknown. Public domain.
Page 168-169: *Orbis Terrarum Nova et Accuratissima Tabula*, 1658, Nicolaes Visscher. Public domain.

TEMPEST: Volume One
Copyright © 2020 by Natasha Kennedy
Varida Publishing and Resources LCC
Woodinville, WA 98072

ISBN: 978-1-937046-28-6
First Edition, first print, 2020

Printed in China

Thanks

Kickstarter contributors:

Sean & Donna Boisen, Jim & Susan Cleary, Jack & Suzanne Hagelin, Cheryl Hansen, Steve & Carolyn Kennedy, the Larson Family, Ben & Alicia McLaughlin, Rob & Katrina Nelson, and David Lyle Taylor

My models:

Arianna America, Lindsay Kennedy, Jordan Neville, and Megan Marshman

My Faithful Eight:

Donna Boisen, Joci Deak, Antonia Hagelin, Terri, Jonathan Wilson, Glenda Walton, Sharon Quarels, and Suzanne Hagelin

Inspiration

Story and writing:

William Shakespeare, Samuel Johnson, James Boswell, Charles Dickens, C.S. Lewis, George MacDonald, J.R.R. Tolkien, G.K. Chesterton, Whittaker Chambers, Alex Thomas, and Meg Jayanth

Artwork:

PJ Lynch, Eyvind Earle, Gustave Doré, David Mack, Jason Brubaker, Jeff Smith, and Arnie Jorgensen

Cosmology, theology, and mythology:

The Bible, St Augustine, Lindsay Kennedy, Plato, Dante Alighieri, Michael Heiser, Robin Parry, Ray Lubeck, Peter Leithart, and John Sailhamer

CONTENTS

DEDICATED TO

—————— Lindsay ——————

THE LOVE OF MY LIFE

Volume One

TEMPEST

Natasha Kennedy

Dear Reader

My master has told me that a writer is merely a glorified witness. As an aspiring writer, I could not have wanted a better master—not because he is a great writer, but because he is a great witness; one could argue he is the *ultimate* witness.

I write this story because it must be written. I am not a great writer, nor a great man, but I have witnessed great things. I have been a witness to things that cannot stay hidden any longer.

This story has been burning in my chest since it first happened and for many years since. I hoped that time would give me the wisdom and articulation needed to do this story justice, but the more the years go by the more I understand that my writing can never truly tell this story in the way it deserves. However, I know now it would be worse for this story to remain unwritten.

There is no way that I can communicate to you what really happened. Words and artistic talents fail me. However, I can mythologize and simplify the truth enough to tell you a story that you may receive as fiction.

To the men and women of my world—the young, the privileged, the empty and the lost—I write to you because I want you to see what I did when I was in my young and formative years: I saw purpose.

Leonard Levi

An Introduction

to the

Cosmos

Modern science has changed the way we see the Cosmos in the Western world. Humanity feels more infinitely small and insignificant than ever as we look through telescopes and try to calculate the multitudes of galaxies, and even universes, that are out there. We think we understand so much more than the ancients ever did—we laugh at them—and yet with all of our discovery, Westerners seem to know less than ever about our true place in the Cosmos.

Through scientific experimentation and observation, we gain knowledge of the physical, but neglect knowledge of the spiritual or supernatural. We have lost the *meaning* behind the physical.

Yes, science and observation can show us so much, but there are some things beyond our grasp: things we could only know if we were *told*—and what if, as with the *Flammarion Engraving*, we could be shown a door to the outside of our physical shell, and we could see the whole of the Cosmos in all its parts?

The *Cosmos* is simply the order and purpose of the universe

The Flammarion Engraving | 1888 | Artist Unknown

when seen in its whole. Growing up in the modern era, I was taught that the Cosmos consisted of matter, elements, planets, stars and the ever-continuing universe that was far too big to comprehend. While this holds some truth, it is but one or two parts of the whole of existence.

The ancients thought of things differently. Rather than trying to figure out *what* the universe is made of and *how* it came into being, they sought to understand the purpose behind *why* things are the way they are. They believed that the world was flat—and in a way they were right—in that the Earth is just one layer of many in the Cosmos, with supernatural realms both above it and below it. In this story, you will find a somewhat Dantean world not unlike what the ancients knew and believed.

The Cosmos is made up of seven layers. Starting from the top and moving downward are: the Heavens, the Waters Above, Raqia, Space, the Lowlands, the Waters Below, and the Underworld.

Whether high or low, every layer of the Cosmos has a purpose and a reason for its existence. Having first been a student of science in my younger years, and then a student of the Cosmos in later ones, I can safely say that it makes a difference in one's life to know the meaning of things and to have a reason to live another day. Whenever I start to despair, or lose my way, I look to the stars and remember: there is a purpose greater than me, and yet I am one of its parts.

How do I know any of this? Well, I was told.

The Seven Layers of the Cosmos

The Heavens *(the Great Temple):* The dwelling place of the Light of Lights and His council. The creator of all life sits enthroned in this place; one too wonderful for me to know or describe.

The Waters Above *(the Glassy Sea, the Flood):* These are the waters of life that flow from the Light of Lights. The pure waters are held above the rest of creation by a hard surface of unbreakable glass.

Raqia *(the Table World):* Raqia is the name given to the table world that is held above the stars by four great pillars whose foundations rest in the four Lowlands. This place is home to the Watchers—the *fae*—who live in an uncursed world of beauty.

Space *(the Great Expanse):* This is the great expanse that separates the Heavens from the Lowlands. This space is insurpassable by mortal man. Placed inside this expanse are the heavenly bodies such as the Sun, Moon, and Stars. Divine spirits dwell within these celestial lights and rule over the Lowlands through the changing of the seasons.

The Lowlands: The Lowlands are the dwelling places of mankind. They include Earth, Paidion, and two other worlds. Cursed with death, its inhabitants have a short lifespan before returning back into the ground from which they were made, in a contnuing cycle of life and death.

The Waters Below *(the Sea):* The waters surrounding and beneath the Lowlands represent de-creation and chaos. Just as the Waters Above bring life, the Waters Below lead to death. The Sea is believed to be the only entrance to the Underworld, concealing the gates to Death.

The Underworld *(Death, Hades, Sheol, or the Great City):* The Underworld is the land where the souls of the dead dwell along with shades and outcast spirits. It is a place of shadow and fire, where the ruler of Death reigns and resides.

CHAPTER I

In which

The Heir is Given His Inheritance

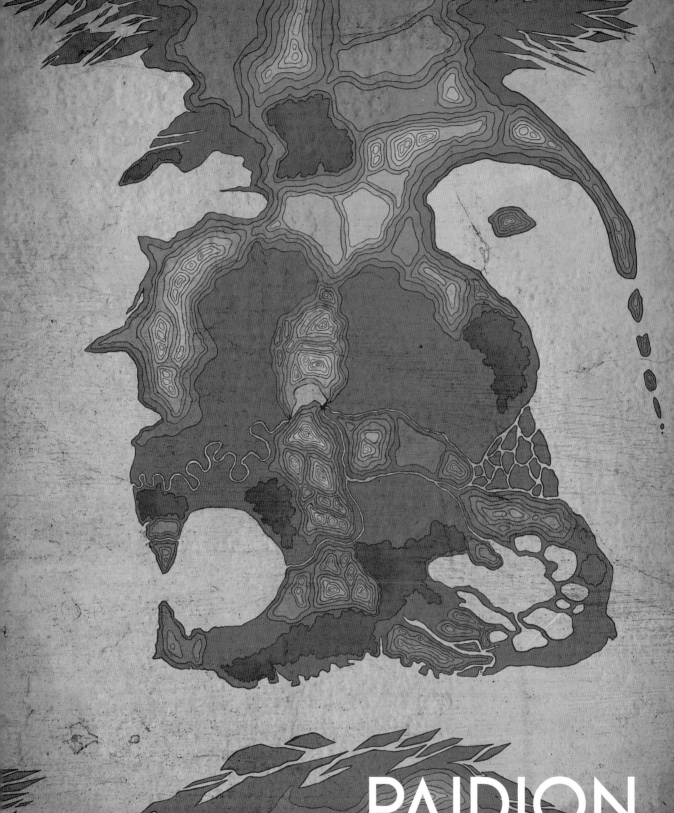

PAIDION

PAIDION IS a child world. She is the younger sister to her brother Earth, being one of the four lowlands containing created beings.

Though her inhabitants have existed for several thousand years, she is still relatively young compared to Earth. The common tongue is an old form of English (the reasons for this, I will explain at a later time). Their whole world is almost entirely united under this one tongue, except for some of the few tribes who exclusively use the Ancient Scrypt.

Much like in early Earth history, their known world stretches across a single continent, which they call Paidion. Anything happening beyond the raging waters of their coasts—if there is indeed anything there—doesn't take place in my story and I have little knowledge of it.

The main inhabitants are a race, alike in almost every way to humans, called Stomen. Originally "Stone men," this name refers to the unique stone on the back of every male's neck, which is ceremonially removed at birth. Stomen occupy approximately a third of the continent and are split into two rival Kingdoms: the Northe and the Southe.

KING ROSHT
OF THE
NORThE

KING DIETRIK
OF THE
SOUThE

For as little as twenty years, there has been a time of peace between Assym of the Northe and Salemn of the Southe. After being at war for centuries, the opposing kings found a peculiar and most surprising friendship in one another. They believed that if they could 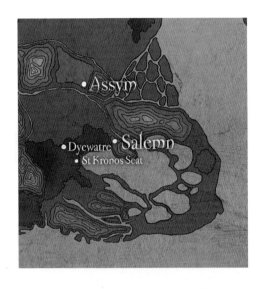 find unity and common ground as men, then they might be able to navigate a way for their nations to do the same.

An alliance was formed; however, this new collaboration brought with it many complications for the once rival nations. The Northe, with its suffering economy, would benefit from Southern aid and the Southe could thrive without the costs of war. Peace-keeping has been a complicated and tiring pursuit, but the two kings have striven to build a bond of friendship between their nations and leaders.

These two kings placed their hopes in the future marriage of their respective heirs in order to secure the nations' precarious relationship. The Northe and the Southe might truly become one if their bond were as strong as blood.

"The beginning is the most important part of any work, especially in the case of a young and tender thing; for that is the time at which the character is being formed and the desired impression is more readily taken."

–Plato

SALEMN
PAIDION

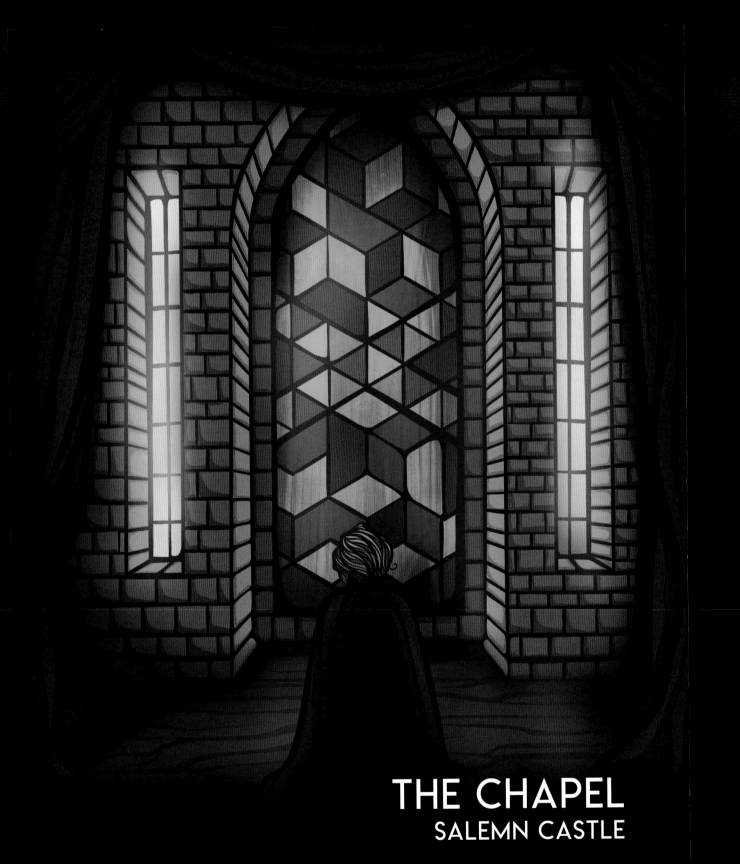

THE CHAPEL
SALEMN CASTLE

Prince Bazil of Salemn, son of King Dietrik of the Southe, was 25 years of age on this day—the day he was to become crowned prince and heir to the throne of the Southe. Knowing that he would be rigorously tested by the elders, Bazil had prepared for this day his entire life. In the Northe, a king's firstborn—whether tyrant or otherwise—would simply inherit the throne. However, the Southe owed its longstanding stability to a board of ministers who voted to appoint a new king and held them accountable to the laws.

I have known many privileged men in my life who took their status for granted or grew comfortable with favour, but I have always been perplexed and inspired by Bazil's retelling of this day: how sober and terrified he was. It was neither modesty nor cowardice that terrified him; it was a raw, naked realization simply of who he was and what he was about to take upon himself. It was exactly what a good and decent man would think when being offered power. That was Bazil: a good man.

"It is the most decisive day of my life." Bazil clenched his fists tightly. "I am not ready in my heart; I am waiting for peace."

"You are ready for the tests, my prince; why are you so heavy?" said a voice from behind.

Bern, the prince's lifelong tutor had come to usher him to the ceremony. It was a usual thing for Bern to find the young prince in this small and quiet chapel, which had no grand purpose in the castle other than for these visits.

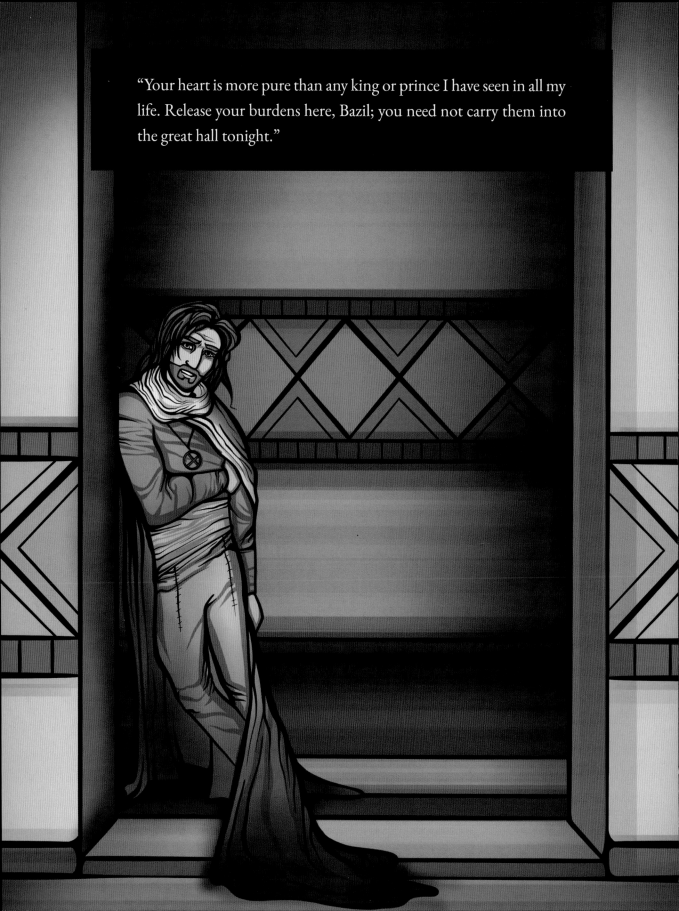

"Your heart is more pure than any king or prince I have seen in all my life. Release your burdens here, Bazil; you need not carry them into the great hall tonight."

tests."

Bern stepped closer. "You will *not* fail the tests, my lord."

Bazil slowly turned to face Bern. "What will I say if I am asked about the Border Tribes?"

"Just speak the truth; you have nothing to hide."

"The truth is not what they want to hear. How can I lead a nation that loves what I hate?"

"You must lead in confidence, not in fear. Like a father, you must teach those you lead in what is right."

"Yes, but what if *my* fathers and mentors are trying to lead me in righteousness, but I do not believe what they teach is righteous? Am I the disobedient one? Am I the naive one?"

You are of age now, Bazil, you have the right to speak as an equal to these men. They must listen."

"They must take me as I am, but I will not deceive them; they need to know how I will lead. And my greatest fear is that they will not want me."

"They would never refuse the son of Dietrik. You are the king they have been waiting for."

"I fear I am *not* what they are waiting for. *That* is why I will fail."

Bern grasped Bazil's shoulder. "You will not fail, Bazil—not while your father sits on the throne. The ministers *must* hear truth and reason."

Bazil stood with confidence. "Yes, you are right. If what I believe is true, it should stand in the presence of the elders."

"—and be persuasive. You have a right to speak now; use it."

Bazil bowed his head to his mentor. "You have been everything to me; I will not forget your counsel." His eyes grew damp.

"It is time, my prince. Be joyful and remember: it is the day of your wedding!" Bern took his hand warmly. "No tears today."

Bazil nodded, recovering from his moment of vulnerability, and advanced determinedly out of the quiet chapel and towards the great hall.

Bazil's heart throbbed as he took each step purposefully towards his future.

This should be the happiest day of his life, yet the pang of terror coiled once again around his stomach. This may become the *worst* day of his life. His success in becoming king rested on his ability to please the ministers, but his success as a man rested on his integrity. Why did those two pursuits feel so at odds?

Taking a deep breath, Bazil entered the great hall where the citizens of his lands had gathered to watch him.

The hall of his father, and his father's fathers, hung high over his head, reminding him of the divine and the eternal. As he walked, a multitude of faces followed him. Yet how many were looking down at him from the stars, gasping and sighing over every word he would say in this trial?

If I am to be a king, he thought, *I will answer for my every word and deed one day. Oh God, help me.*

The event was grand, indeed. Banners hung from every possible height on all sides of the room, light pouring in through the open air at every angle. The march past the crowds towards the head table felt like an eternity as Bazil carefully set one foot in front of the other on the polished stone floor. He finally reached the ministers' table, which was so shrouded in drapery that the majority of the onlookers were unable to see the elders in their lofty seats.

The herald stood in front of the head table, ready to direct the ceremony.

These somber ruling ministers of the Southe were seated on their thrones behind their long regal table. At the centre of them were seated the two kings. Bazil's own father, King Dietrik, locked eyes with his son. Bazil stared at his father carefully as he took in one last deep breath. *Today*, he said in his heart, *the heavens will decide my fate.*

"Presenting Prince Bazil, son to King Dietrik of the Southe," bellowed the voice of the herald, who stood at the front center of the assembly.

The king nodded at his son in approval, filling Bazil with strength.

Bazil knelt down before the thrones and declared in a loud voice, "I submit myself to the tests, that I might become heir to the throne. I have reached twenty-five years of age and have spent my entire life training under my father. I believe I should be considered for the next king of the Southe."

"Prince Bazil will submit himself to the testing of the elders of the Southe for the eligibility of heir to his father's throne," cried the herald, loud enough for all to hear.

"Let the elders of the Southe speak," King Dietrik cried out. The hall fell silent and the assembly waited with anticipation. Bazil held his breath.

One of the elders raised his finger and rose deliberately to his feet. The congregation of citizens filling the hall was still, as every ear inclined to hear the first question that would be put to their future king.

"The minister of the people will speak," declared the herald.

The minister cleared his throat. "I need to know you will put the people's needs before your own. How can I know you are a man of the people and not a man for yourself?"

"I am a man of the people," replied Bazil. "I have for many years now spent the late morning hours of every day walking amongst the streets of Salemn, becoming acquainted with the people and their various needs. I have sought to be one with them so that I might know the strength of the legs on which I will stand as a king. The people will be my second-highest priority in decision-making. I believe that a king is merely a servant to his people, therefore I must hold their well-being in a high regard."

"You will make pleasing the people the 'second-highest' priority? What, then, will be your *first?*" the minister returned.

Bazil became increasingly aware of the expectations of the ever-watching crowd as they awaited his answer. "Keeping the law must come first. For, how can I lead people if I am not also subject to authority? I must also be watched over."

"I am satisfied," declared Pann, Minister of the People, and he seated himself.

Hardly a moment passed before another elder lifted his finger into the air and was announced by the herald. "The Minister of the Treasury will speak."

The Minister of the Treasury rose. "How can we trust you to manage the wealth of the kingdom collected by taxes and the prosperity of growth?"

"Whether the nation is in a season prosperity or famine, I will entrust the management of the finances to the Minister of the Treasury. For any large expense, the entire board of ministers must vote. I will keep my hands away from the kingdom's money and live off an acceptable allowance for the running of the castle."

"Will you maintain the clause that the king has authority to

overthrow the decision of the elders when it comes to financial decisions?" The minister eyed him carefully.

"No, I will remove that clause, keeping the king's hands away from corruption." There was a murmur among the people, and Bazil couldn't tell whether it was approving or not.

Bazil saw a look of surprise and relief in the face of the treasurer, but as he glanced across the table of ministers, he saw a look of distaste on the face of Rosht, king of the Northe.

Bazil quickly dropped his eyes to the floor.

"I am satisfied," said the treasurer, and he rested himself once more on his throne.

Another elder raised a finger. The herald cleared his throat. "The Minister of God will speak."

Traditionally, the religious order known as the Kronosians always had a representative on the council of ministers. Their role was to advise and be involved, but never to vote or excersize power. Elde Galding, the long-standing head of the Kronosian Monks, was one such representative at Bazil's trial.

"Prince Bazil," a gravelly yet articulate voice came from the elderly priest. "Where does your submission to the laws of God fall in relation to the laws of men? Where does this lie in your priorities and how will you receive correction for your own *morality* as king?"

Bazil took a deep breath. "I would be a king second and a man first. I will submit myself, as all men should, first to the laws of God. If I act in any way unbefitting of a king *or* a man, I will trust the Minister of God to bring this to my attention. If I will not listen to correction, the elders may require me to step down for a time until my behavior is satisfactory. In this case, the elders would rule the nation until my return."

This response brought forth a roar of voices in the congregation. "A bit extreme," King Rosht murmured to Dietrik, "too much power to the ministers." He clearly intended to be heard by the rest of the table.

Bazil tensed.

"As mentioned before," the young prince continued faithfully. "I must submit myself to the laws of my country. However, I will not submit if that law does not align with the righteousness of all men. Moral law must come first."

"That is a dangerous statement!" The court fell dead silent as the king of the Northe boldly spoke out of turn.

"Are you saying you will become a law-breaker if your personal beliefs say so?" This kind of intrusion was expected from this infamously temperamental king. All eyes turned now to Bazil.

"No, I will not become a law-breaker, for that is also against my beliefs."

"Then how do you reconcile these statements?" threatened the king.

The Minister of God interjected with a single cough. "I also wish to hear the answer to this question, but may I respectfully remind your majesty that it is still my session?" He stared at Rosht with no sign of timidity. The king of the Northe sat down.

"I will keep the law as king; with the authority of a law-maker, I will make new laws that support the laws of righteousness to the best of my knowledge and ability."

"I am satisfied, young prince." The priest smiled, nodded in Bazil's direction, then sat down.

No sooner did the old man settle onto his throne than King Rosht struck his hand into the air, determined to be the next challenger of the future king. He rose swiftly, his large figure towering over the other elders, before waiting for his announcement.

The herald fumbled in surprise. "Rosht, foreign minister and king of the Northe will speak!"

"How will you, as king, pursue relationships with other nations?" Rosht began with an aggressively raised voice. "Will you continue on your father's path in those relationships? Will you affirm and pursue the alliance with the Northe as your father does?"

Bazil wrestled within himself, keeping the symptoms of fear at bay, then opened his mouth to speak.

"I will continue to pursue peace with the Northe. The fruit of my father's peace-making can be seen throughout our land. Both nations prosper without the grievous costs and losses of war and the new bustling trade between us flourishes. The day the war ended marks the beginning of a new age and we must endeavor to preserve it."

Rosht nodded carefully. This was, evidently, what he wanted to hear. "And will you continue to send aid to the Northe: food, military or otherwise?"

"As long as it remains necessary for the Northe to receive aid to thrive, we will send help for its people."

Rosht squirmed at the cagey response.

Bazil locked eyes with the monarch. "However—" Bazil paused for a second as Rosht narrowed his brow, then continued. "I will not follow my father's steps regarding his military choices. The Northe may need military aid to maintain stability within their walls, but I will not support the attacks on the Border Tribes."

The hall erupted in a clamor of angry voices and gasps of shock. Bazil looked only at his father, who stared at him in disbelief.

"Explain yourself!" the King of the Northe screeched. The herald raised his hands to the congregation, commanding silence.

"The Tribes need not be enemies of our nations," Bazil's voice quivered. "They are small and pose no threat against us, yet we hunt them like animals."

"They *are* animals!" Rosht scoffed.

"They are men and women, like us, with the capacity to do right or wrong," Bazil retorted.

The king's face grew dark and enraged, his body visibly shaking.

"They are a cursed race: evil in their very being! The writings themselves say to '*seek out and kill the beasts, this is will of God*'—will you deny the writings? You claim you want to obey God."

"The translations for that text are complex," returned Bazil, "and it would be unwise to be so dogmatic on it. It was written in a time where those tribes were said to be strong and threatened destruction to the Stomen Kingdom. It is not the case anymore; the Tribes are an oppressed people threatened by extinction due to *our* attacks!"

"Good! *That* is the will of God!" Rosht crowed.

"But how can this view reconcile with the writings that also prophesy about all tribes being united under the Stone again?"

"This isn't a Kronosian debate!" the king bellowed with a stomp of his foot and spit streaming from his mouth. "This is about keeping peace between our nations. Do you forget that the Northe and Southe united in our common war against the Tribes?"

Bazil paused and glanced at his father. "Is this true?"

Rosht continued. "the Southe wouldn't even begin to consider an alliance with a nation seeking to make peace with our greatest enemies—enemies whose very nature cries out to be destroyed!" Rosht marched down toward Bazil until he was nose to nose. Bazil clenched his fists, mustering every bit of courage he had left, as he focused his eyes on his enraged superior.

"I don't think that ceasing our attacks on the Tribes has to mean breaking our bonds of peace," he said softly.

"It *absolutely* does, and I could *never* support a king who would threaten our bond of peace when it has only just begun."

"And *I* could not support an alliance founded merely on common hatred," Bazil returned. The court gasped as if with one voice.

"I would have you remember, young Bazil, that our common hatred before the alliance was directed towards one another; would you rather return to those days?" Rosht straightened himself, his chin held too high for Bazil to meet his eyes. "I am not satisfied. I submit that you are not fit to be king of this nation. You have the brash, untested, idealistic mentalities of youth and will put your own personal ideals above the needs of your country and your people."

Bazil puffed up his chest. "I submit that this is an untrue conclusion. Every leader was once young, and ideals, if founded on truth and wisdom, can be good. The passion of the young can bring

the wisdom of the old into new fruition in their generation. But if I can't lead the people in the same righteousness that I believe is right for myself, then I am an inconsistent and unfit leader."

"Yes, you *are* unfit!" Rosht roared, and turning to the ministers declared, "I submit an *immediate* vote against Bazil as heir to the throne."

Bazil's chin dropped to his chest—as if this sudden loss of dignity tore away any strength he had left. The words '*you are unfit*' rang in his ears. In this moment, the only shred of comfort he could imagine was the face of his tutor Bern who was watching from the sidelines, staring in disbelief.

King Dietrik stood. Bazil held back, refusing to break down into an embarrassing display of emotion. He waited with only one hope: that his father would defend him.

The king of the Southe spoke clearly and calmly. "The Foreign Minister has submitted an immediate vote against Bazil, will anyone second?"

One of the reigning Ministers rose and said, "I, Minister of the Treasury, second this vote."

"Then," cried Dietrik, "all members of the council who vote to deny Bazil's request must stand now."

After a moment of gasps and murmurs, Bazil dared to look up at his elders. The minister of God, according to his Kronosian tradition, declined to vote. The Minister of Defence and the Minister of the People remained seated, while King Rosht, King Dietrik, and the Minister of the Treasury stood.

"Prince Bazil—" his father hesitated, then continued. "The elders have spoken; your request has been denied."

Commotion erupted in the hall once more. *"Silence!"* The herald cried. Bazil stood slowly, bowed to his leaders, and and raised his head high.

"What is a prince if he is not an heir? What have I in this life if I have no inheritance? I am ashamed to stand before you now. You will not take me as I am, and you will not receive the leadership I have given my whole life to perfect for you. I am a man of exile now and there is no place for me in this land. I will disgrace myself no longer by remaining, and I cannot submit to a leadership that would unite over the hatred of others. I will respectfully leave your presence now and not return." And without another word, Bazil turned, marched down the long aisle, and disappeared into the crowds. Dietrik stood, watching his son's departure, but said nothing. All sense of ceremony disappeared from the room as the crowds began to bustle in bewilderment.

"The court is dismissed!" declared the herald, though his work had been done for him when Bazil took his leave.

The soldiers present began to usher the crowds out of the hall, and the ministers remained, quietly arguing amongst themselves about what must be done. The kings joined each other side by side.

Rosht turned to his friend Dietrik. "I was looking forward to presenting Cymbeline as Bazil's bride today—it would have marked such an important day for our nations. What a disappointment."

Dietrik sighed. "Even if the people will not take Bazil as king, the alliance can still be sealed in their marriage. Are you saying you will no longer take my son as your own son?"

"Do not insult me, old friend. I wouldn't marry off my daughter to an exile!"

"Of course," Dietrik nodded. "If you will excuse me, I must go find my son." And at that, the king of the Southe bowed and left.

THE TUTOR BERN emerged from the crowds and seated himself at one end of the elder's table where two of the ministers sat whispering. "An extremely grieving outcome;" Bern shook his head, "Salemn has lost a good king."

"He could have passed the trial had he not gone head-to-head with Rosht." Enald, the Minister of Defence, leaned back in his chair. "The man controls the voting majority of the board."

"He has an understanding with the treasurer," chimed Pann, the Minister of the People. "We all know that Rosht bribes the treasurer to ensure the aid keeps flowing north."

"It's hearsay." Bern shook his head. "We can't assume the treasurer is pocketing money."

"And yet he lives like a king in his province, and there is no way his lands could provide him with so much wealth," Pann mumbled.

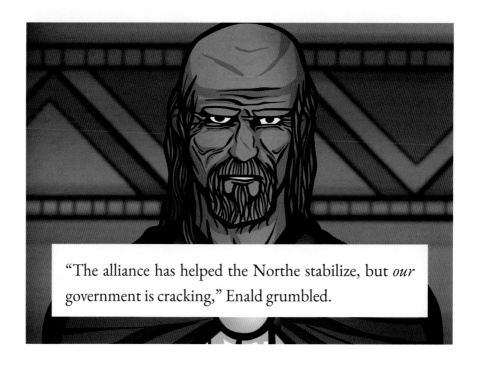

"The alliance has helped the Northe stabilize, but *our* government is cracking," Enald grumbled.

"Well, what can be done?" Bern shrugged. "We needed an end in sight, and now we lost our hope for fresh leadership: we lost Bazil."

Enald slammed his fist on the table. "A tragic loss! The boy might be a pacifist, but he was right about our war with the tribes. It is a joke. Every year I send more and more troops up Northe, and for what—a petty dispute with Border Tribes? The reports I get back make me *sick*. My men are either dealing with uprisings or are out attacking border villages that pose absolutely no threat to the Northe."

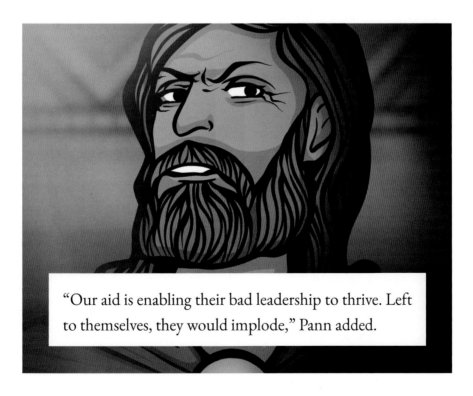

"Our aid is enabling their bad leadership to thrive. Left to themselves, they would implode," Pann added.

"If only Galding had voted. We could have at least continued the trial with a draw." Enald shook his head.

"I may have Kronosian training, but that is one belief of theirs by which I cannot abide. To decline to vote is to deny responsibility; it makes you appear wise while you embrace cowardice. Galding should have voted," Bern looked down at his Crux.

"*You* should be an elder, Bern," said Enald. "It is a shame your wisdom should be wasted on training up a king who will never see the dawn of his reign."

Bern chuckled. "I have no wish to be an elder. I fear that kind of power." He paused, grief filling his heart, "but it is a tragedy that the last ten years of my life have amounted to *this*."

"The fact that you do not desire the role is why you should have it. We could vote you on as the new Minister of God."

Bern shook his head. "No. Change will come, but not that way. We must wait and pray for an opportunity. And then, you must act on it."

Enald and Pann nodded slowly in agreement.

GUEST CHAMBERS
SALEMN CASTLE

ACCORDING TO THE ALLIANCE TERMS, King Rosht had become an honorary member of the southern ministers. His voting rights were seldom executed, as he only visited Salemn for votes that seemed worth his time. The crowning of the future southern heir was certainly an important event to Rosht, and for more than one reason.

Rosht had sons to inherit his own throne in the Northe, but the first-born and only child of his first wife was his daughter Cymbeline. From the day she was born, Rosht had one purpose in mind for her: to marry into the Southe. He knew all too well that a wife has her husband's ear, and that her own wishes soon become her husband's also. In this way, Rosht could have influence on the new king.

Cymbeline had waited in her quarters while the ceremony took place. All she really knew was that, after some time, she would be fetched and presented to Prince Bazil as his bride. It felt like an eternity waiting and she wasn't necessarily excited about the prospect of an arranged marriage. Going from one sovereign master to another felt like no real change. *But*, thought she, *a wife has much more power than a daughter. I think I will prefer being married.*

Cymbeline daydreamed as she waited, wondering what Bazil might think of her when they were finally alone together. In all her life, she only saw him a few times—always in the company of others, and always wearing her veil. In fact, no one besides her parents and maids was permitted to see her face. She was told that her husband alone could be permitted to see her. Yet, there was something about her, she felt, that was shameful. She looked much like her mother, with skin darker than anyone she knew. Her father was always more attached to her mother than to his other wives, yet she too was rarely seen by others. Was there something disgraceful about their origins that Rosht wanted to keep a secret?

"Will Bazil be ashamed of me?" she whispered to herself. "When he sees me—will he be disappointed? I have no idea why he would be; and no idea why he would not!"

"Is there something wrong with me?" Cymbeline said aloud to her mother, turning away from her vanity.

"Of course not," her mother said flatly.

"As you always say," Cymbeline rolled her eyes, "and yet, I feel there is something no one will tell me."

The two women started as the curtained door flew open. They stared in surprised as King Rosht entered the room.

"Shouldn't you be at the ceremony? I was to be brought to you—" Cymbeline attempted to recite the plan that was told to her.

"It's over, girl." He sighed, closed the curtains behind him, then came and took his daughter's face in his hands. "Bazil was denied the throne."

"*What?*" Cymbeline shrieked.

Her mother darted her eyes towards her husband curiously.

"You will not marry the boy; he is an exile now."

"What did you *do,* you snake!" Cymbeline fumed. "You did something, I *know* you did!" She shook him off.

"How *dare* you!" Flushed with indignation, Rosht shoved her to the floor and seized a nearby candlestick.

Cymbeline cowered as he struck a blow across her back. Smarting in agony, Cymbeline turned her face towards her father once more. "I wanted to marry him, you *bastard!*"

Scarcely had she spoken before another heavy blow fell across her shoulder. She uttered a scream of pain as he brandished his instrument of torture. Her mother watched lifelessly.

"Defy the king again!" Rosht spat.

Cymbeline froze, wincing in pain and clutching at her trembling body. Slowly, she dropped down onto her knees and bowed her head to the floor in submission.

Rosht raised the candlestick once more above his head.

"My love," the queen interjected softly. "What is to be done now?"

The king lowered his weapon and glanced at his wife with an eerie smile. "Dietrik is left without an heir and without a wife, Temmy."

"He is, indeed?" The queen grinned and joined her husband at the arm. The two of them walked toward the door, but before exiting Cymbeline's chambers, Rosht turned to her and muttered, "you are not to leave the room until we send for you."

BAZIL'S CHAMBERS
SALEMN CASTLE

After his humiliating failure, Bazil had shut himself in his chambers and took to packing every item he thought he might need on the road to exile.

"I can't believe they would vote against the son of Dietrik! You were not even given a full trial," said Bern, who was stewing by the door; "—your own *father*!"

"What's done is done," Bazil said frustratedly. "I would rather the trial end prematurely if the outcome would be the same; I could not endure further shame."

Dietrik entered the room unexpectedly. Bazil behaved as if there was no change, and Bern hurriedly knelt down with his face toward the floor.

"You can't just leave; you can't just abandon your position!" The king demanded.

"Father, I am unwanted. My life's work and my future have been taken from me; it is my right to leave," said Bazil. He was busying himself with his packing, refusing to make eye contact.

"Just give me some time, son. I can talk through some of these things with you, and when you recant some of your words, I can overthrow this decision!"

Bazil froze and then turned towards his father. "You think that would bring back my honour? It would be going against *everything* I believe about accountability. How could I live with myself if my very foundation is a farce? You have a peace treaty to worry about—I am only a hindrance to you now."

"Bazil," Dietrik stepped forward and took his arm. "Sometimes as a king you need to make compromises and let go of the small in order to hold on to the great. Can you not let go of this *one, small* thing?"

"How could you ask this of me?" Bazil's voice cracked. "Did you not hear any word I said in the trial? This is not *small* to me, and it's not small to you either, though neither you nor King Rosht will see it. The only honourable path left to me is to leave and accept the decision of the elders. I will leave tonight."

"You are allowed to disagree, just keep your disagreements to yourself until you are king, and then you can do as you please! The people will follow your leadership."

"'*One can only lead those who will follow.*' I can not be their true leader if they do not wish to follow my leadership."

Deitrik turned towards Bern and looked down at him with restrained displeasure. "You would not have done this if you didn't have this—this free-thinking *anarchist* for a tutor."

Bern tensed, his face still down towards the ground.

Bazil wagged his head at his father. "Bern is my tutor, but you are my father. It is *you* who taught me to love righteousness and justice. It is you who must take responsibility for raising me, and I

who must take responsibility for my choice. Bern must be blamed for nothing."

"Bazil, you can't just—"

"Please, show me the respect of honouring my decision and leave me. *Please*. Both of you."

Without another word, Dietrik marched out of the room in a rage. Bern said nothing to Bazil as he rose from the floor and, with a gentle squeeze of his friend's shoulder, left him alone.

In his solitude, Bazil wept.

Several hours later, Bazil sat alone in his tutor's study, pouring through maps in the late hours of the night. The room was dimly candle-lit, so Bazil did not see that Cymbeline had entered the room until she was within arm's reach.

"Princess!" Bazil raised his head in surprise and met her eyes. "It's late, do your attendants know you're here?" He shifted in nervous discomfort.

Cymbeline rolled her eyes dramatically. "Why is everyone so *concerned* about that?" She was slightly taken aback by Bazil's indifference to her appearance.

Though he had always seen her veiled, it was not hard for him to figure out who she was: firstly because of her recognizable voice and demeanor and secondly, it was not hard to note her royal attire. Bazil put down his map, crossed his arms, and leaned back to give her his full attention. He couldn't guess why the mysterious princess had decided to pay him a visit, but he supposed that now he was in exile he would hear her out. "What can I do for you, my princess?"

"Are you not even thinking about the fact that we were supposed to be *married* tonight?" Cymbeline slammed her hands on the table across from him and leaned forward. Bazil blushed at the frankness of her question. Before this moment, they had virtually been strangers.

"I am thinking about many things, my princess, including that fact," he answered honestly.

"And you weren't going to come talk to me about it?"

"It has never been a liberty of mine to come and talk freely with you, princess. It was a political marriage; I did not think you would be disappointed when it did not take place."

"You think that because I am a woman, I will not care what happens to me?"

"No, I don't think that at all. If anything, I assumed this

marriage put pressure on you—as it did me—and that you would be glad that it did not take place."

"Granted, I wasn't happy about being married for advantage, but I would rather you than anyone else my father had in mind!"

"I am sorry, princess, it was not my plan to be denied; I would have gladly married you." He stared at her, expressionless, repressing the grief he still felt about his failed trial.

"So, you—you *wanted* me?" She lowered her voice.

"I was ready to do my *duty*, and that included marrying you

and pursuing you for the rest of my life. I'm sorry that it will never be. I did want it."

Cymbelline collapsed in a heap of defeat on the chair across from Bazil with her face in the palm of her hand, the disappointment hitting her all over again. "It's not like I wanted to get married, but what if I *did* want to get married?" She stared at him, waiting for an answer. She eyed him suddenly with a doubtful scowl. "I mean—haven't you thought about the fact that we would have been *together* tonight?"

Bazil flushed a deep red. "I was very overwhelmed by the trial, I confess I was not thinking as much about the wedding aspect."

"Oh come now; you must have *thought* of it!"

"It is not a conversation I wish to have with you. We are no longer bethrothed and I don't want to be guilty of any misconduct towards you."

Cymbeline moaned in frustration. "You don't have to be so *proper*, Bazil. You're leaving forever. I just thought that for once you and I could talk as equals without all the pomp and ceremony—or that at least I could just have a pedestrian conversation with you, if nothing else."

Bazil nodded his head slowly. "I can understand that." He sighed. "Then, what would you like to talk about, Cymbeline?"

Cymbeline sat up straight, surprised that her words had any impact on a man. "Well—"

Bazil held up a finger and quickly added, "nothing regarding my thoughts about our wedding."

"Fair enough." She trilled her fingers on the table with a thoughtful expression. "Well, where are you planning on going?"

"Well," he pointed down at a map lying open on the table. "I have been looking through Bern's maps and I see he has marked *this* as a good place to stop on a journey. See here?—this place is called '*Dyewatre Inn.*' Do you see this marking?"

She leaned in for a closer look. "Yes, but I don't know what it means."

"From studying his maps, I presume he puts this mark on places outside of our borders where he has stayed. This one must be friendly to Stomen. If I say his name, they might welcome me in!"

"Your tutor has travelled outside the borders?"

"Yes, he is a well-travelled man and wise teacher. He taught me everything I know about the Tribes."

"What is there to know?" Cymbeline asked naively.

"The fact that you know nothing proves there is everything to know. They are almost entirely a mystery to Stomen." Bazil looked up at Cymbeline with—for the first time that day—excitement.

"You plan on going and finding them, don't you?"

"Where else have I to go? I have no place here. I must start my journey *somewhere*, and I have always longed to travel outside our borders."

"So you're starting with this place, '*Dyewatre*'?"

"Well, that is at least a week's travel. I'll start *here*." Bazil pointed at a place on the map just on the border. "It is a Kronosian monastery just outside the border. I will reach it in a few days, perhaps stay there a while, and then make my way towards Dyewatre on the day following. And there, perhaps I will find more direction."

Cymbeline nodded, hoping to communicate her approval when she really had no idea what to think.

"Is this a nice conversation?" He looked up at her with a sincere smile.

"Well, it is not very *pedestrian*; you are talking about travelling to places I will never see or experience."

"Why does this make you sad? You couldn't possibly be jealous of exile."

"You have no idea. I couldn't choose exile if I wanted to! I am merely a slave to my country: to my father's wishes. Exile sounds like liberty to me."

"We are all slaves to duty."

"I know that! But can't I be jealous of the man who found a way out of his?" She stood in agitation.

"Cymbeline, I would give my life if it meant I could do my duty!" said Bazil, rising also, and taking slight offence at her words.

"So just *do it!* Tell them what they want to hear, and then you can marry me and we can both do our duty without misery!"

"What you suggest is impossible; must I explain this to *everyone?* My duty is to have integrity. I cannot be king without it."

"I know you won't be convinced, Bazil. You will leave and I will remain. It is the way it must be, I suppose." She stared at him hopelessly.

The two stood facing each other, wordless. Bazil, in an uncharacteristic moment of impropriety, put his hand on her shoulder. "You would not have wanted me, Cymbeline."

"But I *did*." Tears escaped down her cheeks.

"You are strong; I see it now. You can find happiness for yourself, if you want to."

"Do you think so?" she sniffed.

"Yes, I do."

"Could I come with you?"

"Don't be foolish." Bazil broke the quiet moment with a sudden dive back into his maps. "I would never dishonour you or your father by allowing you to come with me on such a perilous journey. It would be treason."

"I know." She glanced down, wishing she hadn't voiced her request.

"Good bye, Cymbeline, I have enjoyed this real moment with you."

"Thank you, Bazil. I have as well."

By morning, Bazil had left through the city gates.

It is not until you truly give up something precious that you find out how much you wanted it. Once it is gone, the deep, endless feeling of death creeps into your heart, and the realization of its finality causes you to change. If the presence of a thing affects who you are and what you do, then its absence will do so even more. As it dies, a part of you dies, and you will then find yourself searching for a new thing to fill its empty, desolate place.

Bazil was a changed man after his disappointing trial, but it was not until he actually left Salemn that he truly felt the death of his future life. The road of the unknown border country stretched out before him, as did the mysterious road of his future. He was once filled with purpose, conviction, and certainty, and now he was not only a man with nothing, he was a man with a hopelessly endless crevice of loss in his heart. This wound would change him, for better or for worse.

One can only imagine where this road of uncertainty will take our ex-prince as he leaves his once-future behind, but I can guarantee that what awaits him in his future will be far more precious to him than what he left behind.

GUEST CHAMBMERS

SALEMN CASTLE

One week had passed. Bazil was long into his journey onward while Cymbeline remained with her parents in Salemn. Their plan was to return Northe on the following day. Cymbeline was, as always, left alone in her room while her parents spent the evening elsewhere.

She sat on her chaise lounge for a while thinking about Bazil's adventures out in the unknown, wishing there was some way she could have gone with him. For her whole life, Cymbeline had been told that she was to marry this man, and so she had prepared herself for the freedom that would have come with her marriage. Instead of remaining in the Southe to be her own person, she was to return to the Northe as—once again—her father's prisoner.

Impulse drove her to peer through the door into the hall to see if anyone was there.

There was a time when guards used to enforce her curfew, but eventually her own fear was the only enforcement needed. Knowing that this was her last night in Salemn gave her just enough drive to sneak through the door and wander down the hall

Cymbeline had not gone far before she was by the door to her father's chamber. Voices further down the hall enticed her to wander further. At the end of the hall was an open balcony, where she saw her father sitting next to King Dietrik. From here, they could not see her.

Leaping quickly behind a large velvet curtain, she held her breath, hoping she wasn't spotted. After a few moments of collecting herself, Cymbeline began to overhear words in the conversation between the two kings. Not wanting to be discovered, she kept herself hidden and listened carefully.

THE CONVERSATION
———— Between ————
KING ROSHT AND KING DIETRIK

DIETRIK: "...he left because we denied him his throne."

ROSHT: "He forced our hands."

DIETRIK: "What's done is done. We must agree on how to proceed."

ROSHT: "What of the alliance? The marriage would have secured it forever."

DIETRIK: "Without a son, what else have I to offer?"

ROSHT: "Who is next in line?"

DIETRIK: "There is no one—no one agreed upon."

ROSHT: "And what will happen if you die without an heir? What will happen to the kingdom?"

DIETRIK: "You know the answer to this, Rosht. The elders must vote on a new king, though I cannot imagine whom."

ROSHT: "The answer is before you: Cymbeline is young and ready to marry. Marry her and produce an heir."

Cymbeline restrained a gasp.

DIETRIK: "At my age? No—it is not the answer."

ROSHT: "Are you that old? A pity—your line is indeed frail."

DIETRIK: "You are no younger than I am, Rosht. I am, in fact, two years younger than you."

ROSHT: "You should know by now, Dietrik, that I am cut from a different cloth than you; I will be young long after you are dead."

THE CONVERSATION
Between
KING ROSHT AND KING DIETRIK

Dietrik: "Don't let the faerie magik deceive you. Age affects us all and I, unlike you, have embraced it."

Rosht: "Entrust your kingdom to me, Dietrik. Then, our nations will be united at last."

Dietrik: "Watch yourself, Rosht."

Rosht: "Fight me while you can, friend, but just give it time; I will remain as I am, while you waste away. You and your line will perish, and I will still be here—king of the Northe *and* the Southe."

—

The conversation came to an abrupt end; suddenly all Cymbeline could hear was shuffling, muffled cries, and a foreign tongue spoken by deep, rugged voices. Her heart raced as she dared to peek through an opening in the curtain. What she saw proved Rosht's final words to be somewhat ironic.

CHAPTER II

In which

The Wanderer Finds
His Purpose

RAQIA

Fero
Lands

Paradise
• Valley

Raqian
Woodlands

WHAT WOULD IT BE LIKE to wander a world with no sun or moon? Here, day and night change at their own will with little reference to time. The unkempt flora tames itself, dancing as it happily exists with perfect purpose.

Raqia: the uncursed world. Yes, Death came to it—he found a way—but his authority and influence is limited. These lands are covered in life that grows without restraint and is inhabited by creatures who live in contentment. Nights are never cold enough to wear a covering and the pleasant heat of the day is never oppressive enough to cause one to perspire. All water is life-giving to drink, vegetation thrives without coaxing, and the land—as ordered by its king—gives its dwellers everything they could ever need.

Many of us on Earth dream of journeying into distant and wild lands, leaving everything behind us and following our every whim. Few truly escape the responsibilities that pull us back home. If one were able to experience such a journey, he could do no better than to set out into the lawless, uncharted woodlands of Raqia. However, not only is the topography too complex and labyrinthine to map, but the endless mystical reports and eerie tales about it rightly keep every level-headed traveler far away.

Only the fickle Woodland Elves dare to live on the edge of this forest. Though drawn to its perplexing, spiritual aura, they are rightfully fearful of the spirits that dwell within the wilderness. Thus, no inhabitant has ever set foot inside—except one: Clover.

NOWHERE
RAQIAN WOODLANDS

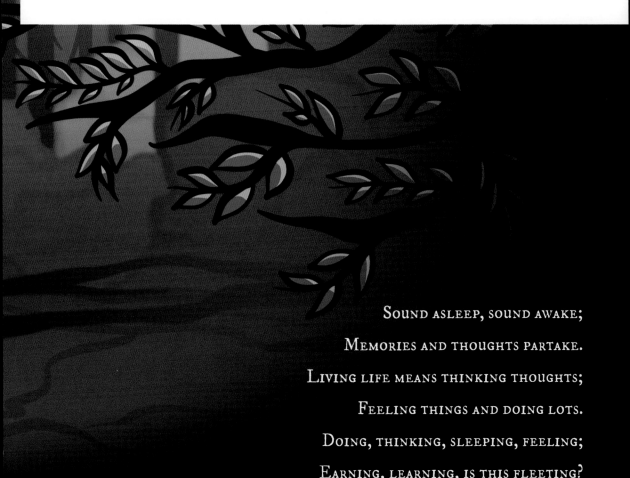

Here, amongst the twisting paths and dense forest depths of the Raqian Woodlands, we join our wandering Elf as he meanders aimlessly towards no-where-in-particular. It is through Clover, this amateur Elven poet, that you will first experiece a quiet walk through the holy lands of Raqia.

Sound asleep, sound awake;
Memories and thoughts partake.
Living life means thinking thoughts;
Feeling things and doing lots.
Doing, thinking, sleeping, feeling;
Earning, learning, is this fleeting?

Doing left no time for thinking;
Doing only led to sleeping.
Thinking made me run from feeling;
Feeling only ruins sleeping.
Feeling made me question learning;
Question life and question earning.
Circles, circles, round again;
I'll question life until I'm dead.

NOTHING MADE ME WANT TO STAY;

A COIN WAS ALL I HAD THAT DAY.

GOING, STAYING, YES OR NO;

NOTHING BUT THE GOLD TO THROW.

THE COIN SAID GO AND SO I WENT;

I WANDERED OUT WITHOUT BEING SENT.

Untouched by the Death Curse of the lower realms, Raqia is home to a vast array of intelligent fauna. Where we on Earth experience animals with only a certain capacity of communication and development, these Raqian inhabitants have the capacity for language, intelligence, and even simple communities and culture.

We on Earth don't wonder or despair about the creatures in our care when they don't talk back to us—try as they might—but we should. I certainly didn't fret about it before I visited this holy place, but I can assure you that I have spent many hours grieving it since.

UP AND DOWN AND THROUGH THE WOOD;

THINKING, FEELING, WHEN I COULD.

WAS NO MORE LOST THAN WHEN I LEFT;

NOTHING THERE TO FEEL REGRET.

THINKING, FEELING, DOING, SLEEPING;

IT'S ALL THE SAME, IT ALL IS FLEETING.

SUNDER FALLS
RAQIAN WOODLANDS

This seemed, to Clover, a curious place for a common ovis, and and he thought its trivial inclinations the perfect guide into disarray. The thing wandered curiously behind a monstrous waterfall and it seemed natural for him to follow it.

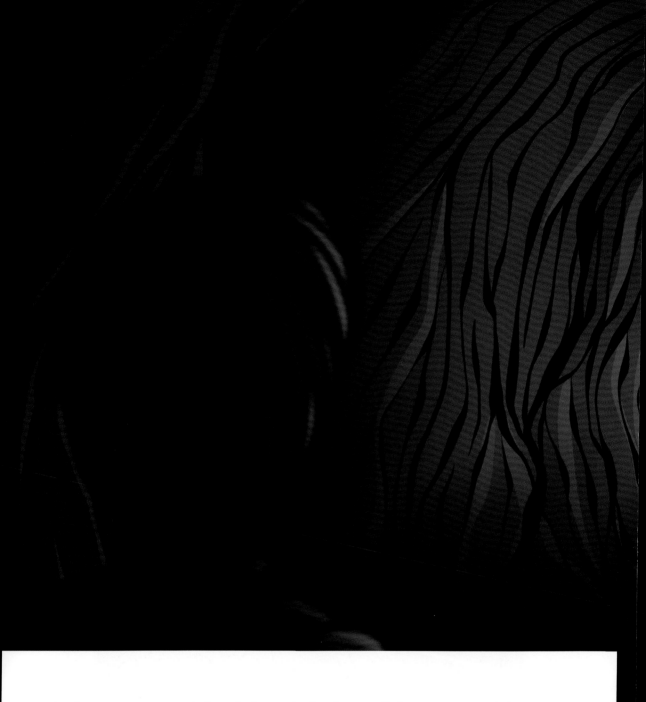

Curling passageways slithered through the heart of the mountain. There were several turnoffs that looked as though they led deeper into the mountain, but the lone sheep continued dead ahead, like an ant following its trail of brothers.

The passage finally opened up into an enclosed valley lit up by a kaleidoscope of colours. The ovis joined many others on a grassy hill, basking in the shade of his—

PARADISE VALLEY
RAQIAN WOODLANDS

Wanting, wanting, something new...

Wanting makes it all askew.

Feeling, doing, sleeping, thinking

Everything I knew is sinking.

"Who is this who looks down like the dawn, beautiful as the night; bright as the day? You have captivated my heart; you have captivated my heart with one glance of your eyes, with one turn of your head, my heart fails within me."

The woman watched in surprise, humour, and interest as she was approached by a wandering elf who suddenly knelt before her.

"Poetry?" she chuckled in amusement.

"Is there any other way to speak to a goddess? You are perfection."

"Perhaps not, but I'm no goddess." The goddess laughed.

"Only one so perfect could be so unaware of her own beauty."

"Not unaware," she smiled. "Just unaffected."

"Tell me who you are."

"Tell me who *you* are! *You're* the stranger skulking around in the woods and detaining unsuspecting women."

"You are correct. I am everything lowly and vile in a presence such as yours. Your beauty makes me a skulker, a nothing, an *imbecile*."

The young woman looked at the elf carefully, unmoved by his response.

"I am called Clover," he said.

"Clover?" she laughed. "Hello, Clover—and who is your sweet little friend there?" The maid pointed down by Clover's feet where a little gnome was attempting to hide.

"Who?" Clover shook his leg loose of the thing. "Get off,

scram!" he spat. "This thieving *scumbag* followed me out here!"

She reached out her hands to the animal. "He is adorable, what's his name?"

"Thieving Scum Bag." Clover shrugged as the thing dashed once more behind his boot.

"Aw, well, that's not a very nice thing to call him!"

"It is, in fact, very fitting; these garden gnomes do nothing but steal from my colony. They are the world's most bothersome pests."

"Well, it was nice, um, meeting you, Clover." The woman rose to leave.

"*Tell me your name!*" gasped Clover in desperation.

"My name is Isabella, if you must know." She seemed, in this moment, almost taken in by his passion.

"Isabella," he took her hand. "From the moment I saw you, I have felt my heart awaken from the dead. You are life itself to me. Tell me you will let me love you; promise me you will never again leave my sight. Give me your hand in marriage and my heart can rest knowing you're mine! I love you—I love you more than anything!"

After staring at Clover in shock for a moment, Isabella burst into laughter. "Love me? You don't even *know* me!"

"Then let me know you so that you can believe my love. I would die for you!"

"I do not believe you could possibly love me, Clover, for you lack one great component for the kind of love that you declare."

"I did not believe in 'love at first sight' until this moment, but I do now. Tell me what you think my love lacks so that I might prove myself to you!"

"Well, I don't believe in 'love at first sight,' for *constancy* is a defining characteristic of love; constancy can only be tested by time."

"It is as you say. Time is the test of constancy, but it does not mean my love is not real, it simply means my love is untested."

"You almost compel me to believe you."

"Charge me with anything... *anything* to prove my love to you."

"I can charge you with something, Clover."

"Anything."

"Then come this way, I will introduce you to my father. If he likes you, then you can marry me." Isabella tightened her grasp on Clover's hand and pulled him toward a cluster of trees in the valley.

"Your *father*?" Clover felt a dreadful pain in the pit of his stomach, but he followed her all the same, foolishly maintaining a hope that her father might give him a second thought.

Want is all I know today;
Wanting makes me feel this way.

Want I have not felt before;
Want is something else and more.

I think and feel and know I want;
You make the coin irrelevant.

I make my choice my choice is best;
It's best because my heart's at rest.

Wanting makes me know its you;
Want is all I know that's true.

Isabella.

HOMESTEAD
PARADISE VALLEY

Isabella led Clover through the small wilderness of trees until they came to a perfectly placed stone house, overgrown with vines and shrubbery. They meandered around to the back of the house where a man of large stature was chopping firewood.

"I have a wandering elf for you, Papa." Isabella nonchalantly gestured towards Clover as her father rose to full height and stared blankly at them then swung his axe again.

"You go on inside, Isabella," grunted the man.

Isabella crossed her arms with a hint of stubbornness. "I am fine where I am, Papa, if you don't mind." She sat down on a garden bench.

He grunted again. "You trying to make love to my daughter?" He spoke without moving a muscle, though it felt to Clover as if he had stepped closer.

Clover crossed his arms haughtily, "Not trying to make anything—but now that you mention it, I do love your daughter."

The intimidating figure took a step closer. "Excuse me?"

"Was that not clear? I love Isabella and I want her. Can I have her?"

The large figure took Clover by the neck and lifted him up against the side of the house. Clover felt, possibly for the first time in his life, terror.

"Papa—" Isabella sighed.

"I was," Clover gasped, "just passing through."

"Papa!" Isabella coughed loudly.

Her father dropped him to the ground. "An elf—just *passing through*? What is your name, elf?"

"Clover."

"Alright, Clover. This is what is going to happen: you will come in, have a short dinner with us, and then you will leave this valley and never return."

"Yes, Sir." Clover refrained from rolling his eyes and followed Isabella into the house.

IN THE HOMESTEAD
PARADISE VALLEY

ISABELLA, her father Joel, and Clover communed for a meal around a small, square table inside the homestead. Joel knew it was a rare thing for his daughter to entertain a guest and humoured her for that reason alone. He eyed the boy with caution as Isabella served her hand-made pies, and tolerated the garden gnome with more favour than he did the elf.

"So tell me, Clover, what brings you to these parts?" Joel attempted small talk.

"Nothing," said Clover flatly.

"Nothing?" Joel growled.

"Well, maybe adventure?"

"*Maybe?* You don't seem to know what you're doing at all! Are you some kind of lost soul? Explain yourself."

"You could say. I have, for most of my life, been lost. It was not until recently I discovered my passion."

"*Recently?*"

Clover gestured towards Isabella, who chuckled behind her hand. Joel groaned.

"So, what's in the bag?" The patriarch eyed Clover's mysterious bag, which he had set beside his dinner on the table.

"The bag? What bag?"

"*That* bag." Joel thrust his index finger towards the only possession Clover seemed to have besides his spear and scroll. "It's an Exsilium Prison; what are you doing with one of those?"

"How am *I* supposed to know?" Clover defensively crossed his arms.

"Isn't it yours?"

Clover nodded his head in the direction of the Thieving Scum Bag. "He must have nabbed it off somebody, and well—I recovered it."

"Well, go on then," he nodded to the bag. "Open it."

Clover glanced back and forth between Joel and Isabella. They both seemed genuinely curious so he shrugged and tugged open the mouth of the sack.

To the great surprise of the younger two at the table, a six-inch tall faerie sat cross-legged in the opening, and stared up at Clover with an unimpressed expression. Rising slowly to a stand, he straightened his attire, looked around the table in surprise, and after carefully studying his rescuer, turned to face the master of the table. With a look of recognition, the faerie's eyes grew wide.

"Thought so." Joel sighed and leaned forward to look down at the new arrival. Clover stared, expressionless, at the little thing.

"A faerie?" Isabella gasped.

"*You*—this is not what I was expecting." The fae searched for words, keeping his eyes locked on Joel's.

"Who were you expecting?" Joel asked.

"Korbin—he imprisoned me."

The father's face darkened. "Korbin? You mean that renegade man-hunter?"

"Yes—he is hunting outlaws for Somenus."

"The *Nightmare Faerie*." Joel bowed his head and sighed.

"Yes, well, that's what the mortals call him. But of course you know him by his true name, my old friend."

A moment of silence passed and Isabella stared at her father in confusion.

"Then, the rumors were true." Joel leaned down towards the fae, eyeing a small gold chain tied to his ankle. The fae only nodded silently.

"Papa, what's all this about?" Isabella took her father's arm and drew his eyes to her.

"Isabella, Clover; leave us."

"Papa! Why can't I—"

"Outside. *Now!*" He broke into a yell.

Isabella frustratedly rose from her table, grabbed Clover by the sleeve, and dragged him outside, slamming the door behind her.

THE MEADOW

PARADISE VALLEY

CLOVER AND ISABELLA sat down together in a patch of soft grass. Clover took this unforeseen chance to speak privately with his obsession once more.

"Do you ever get tired of being told what to do?" he asked, seeing that she was visibly angry.

"No, not really."

"Oh. That's surprising. Your father seems to keep you on a tight leash."

"That's a very pessimistic way of seeing it."

Clover shrugged. "I speak as I find."

"My father is a good leader. I am very well cared for. You can't make me discontent with that."

"I don't mean to make you discontent—I would hate to plague you with the sickness that has infected me for many years now—but don't you ever get lonely out here?"

Isabella paused. "Sometimes. But when I do, I just take a trip to town to sell my mead; I have friends there."

"There's a town out in this wilderness? Wait—*mead*?"

She laughed. "Yes. Yes there *is* a town, though you have to know where to find it."

"Haven't you ever wished to travel further? Surely you have desires beyond just living in this valley, tending sheep, and...*bees?*"

She thought for a moment. "I have often felt there might come a reason to leave here. Something out there for me to do. Is that how you feel?"

"I am infected with wanderlust, curiosity—*starvation*—for a sense of passion." He stopped and looked at her. "And I think you are, too."

Clover laid back into the grass and pointed upwards. "Don't the reflections above us inspire you to find the stars' true source? Don't the rippling flickers just tease you?

"I love the stars." She laid down to join him. "They make me feel like I am the only one for whom they were made."

He replied, "they make me think about the Glassy Sea above us, held up by an unbeakable transparent shell: how its surface reflects the stars in the Raqian Sea below. As I see them sway, move, and sparkle above us, I'm reminded of the sea below: the window to their home. The stars glitter like diamonds in its depths. Sailors, dazzled by their beauty, dive into the deep, thinking them priceless treasures, drowning as they are consumed by obsession."

"Oh, you make me ever so jealous; I have never seen the Raqian Sea! What is it like?"

He closed his eyes and breathed in deeply. "The sands are like powdered crystal: shining like gold in the day and glistening like silver in the night. As you stand on the edge of the land, you behold a monstrous body of water caught in endless, magnificent motion. Layer upon layer of waves hurry towards you, and you wonder how—despite such power, strength, and constant determination—

this force is unable to reach you. With loud claps, the waters crash up against the land beneath your feet and droplets of water reach up to brush your face.

"How can a power as great as the Sea try so hard to reach you and still fail? And you stand still, sensing the tension of opposite forces, feeling both safe and utterly terrified. It is the most beautiful thing I have ever beheld, until tonight." Clover turned to look at the beauty beside him.

She stared back into his face. "You're making it hard to say no to you."

"Don't say no."

Isabella broke the tension with a laugh. "I still don't really know what you're trying to offer me!"

"I am offering you my love. I am offering you adventure. I

am offering you arms to hold you every cold night and legs to lead you to beautiful new places. I am offering you my devotion and my determination to know every bit of you for the rest of my life. I offer you the peace of never again wondering 'who' or 'if.' Take me and I will give you anything you ask. I will give you myself."

Isabella laughed again and stared back up at the stars. "That sounds very appealing."

"But..."

"But I don't *know* you!" She rose swiftly and stared back down towards the homestead. "How am I supposed to know that anything you say is for sure. You are just a mystery who wandered into my valley and something tells me I shouldn't just trust you! What kind of a name is 'Clover' anyway? That doesn't sound Elven to me."

"Well, I do have an Elven name, but I don't think it suits me." Clover stood and drew closer.

"What is it?" She turned to him curiously.

"Trefolian."

"*Trefolian!*—it's beautiful! What does it mean?"

"It is a unique flora made up of three leaves symbolizing devotion: one leaf is cognition, one is action, and the third affection. It grows in the shades of large trees in thick, luscious beds."

"So, a clover...."

"Yes. Common: clover."

"You think you are common?"

"I don't suit the elegance of my kin. My poetry is too vulgar and my manners crude. I prefer to be common—'common,' to me, is far more interesting."

"You're definitely an interesting person, Clover." Isabella looked back toward the house, her mind returning to the mysterious arrival of the faerie. "With an interesting faerie."

"Oh, come now, Isabella! Why think on that dull fae when the affairs of *love* are before you *here*?"

Isabella closed her eyes in deep frustration. "There are things, Clover, things I have been longing to know long before you ever got here."

"Do I make *any* impact on you? Give me some shred of hope!"

"Clover—I..."

"You want to know about that fae."

"I'd like to know about anything!" Isabella shook her fists. "All of these years of keeping secrets; I am not a child anymore!"

"Ah—and there it is." Clover smirked.

"There is what?" She shot him a glare.

"The *discontentedness*. I knew you had it." Isabella's scowl convinced Clover that he might need a different approach to winning her favour.

"Well," he shrugged innocently, "would it interest you to know what they are saying?"

Isabella's annoyance softened and she turned back to look at her persuer. "What do you mean?"

He faked innocence. "I can hear them." He pointed at his Elven ear.

"You can *hear* them? These are the kinds of details I would want to know, Clover! Well, come on; what are they *saying?*"

Clover chuckled and stepped in closer, riding his wave of success. "I'll tell you if you marry me."

"Tell me what they are saying, elf!" She glared.

Clover rolled his eyes. "Well…"

THE CONVERSATION
Between
JOEL AND DEZMUND

JOEL: "So Korbin is working for Somenus?"

DEZMUND: "He is the faerie King now; he needs men to do his dirty work. Who better than Korbin? His army is immense now—and he is sending out his personal minions to capture any fae who resist his rule. He's been personally hunting me down for a year, at least."

JOEL: "Somenus wants revenge, I imagine. I doubt he forgot about you, Dezmund; it was your wound that ended his siege on Arelle two thousand years ago."

DEZMUND: "Well, this time he succeeded—he took the throne and we had no friends to help us, Timbre Wulf; he is setting up rulers all over Raqia."

JOEL: "You are not the first faerie to come my way. I was already approached by two of them and they told me everything. I will tell you what I told them: I am not Timbre Wulf anymore."

Clover and Isabella turned to look at each other.

"Timbre Wulf?" she whispered. "Who in the heavens is Timbre Wulf?"

"You don't know?" Clover looked at her in surprise.

"No one tells me anything—tell me who he is!"

"He was, well..."

"Are we missing the conversation?" she interrupted hastily.

"Yes."

"Well, what are they *saying?*"

Clover closed his eyes and listened.

THE CONVERSATION
——— Between ———
JOEL and DEZMUND

DEZMUND: "Then you may know more than I do. I have been hiding ever since the word got out that Somenus became King. Do you know how it happened? How was he able to kill Faerex? Surely there is no weapon powerful enough."

JOEL: "I'll tell you all I know, my old friend. Two years ago, two fae from the Late Faerex's court came here seeking the legend they called the '*Friend of the Fae*.' They had fled the city after Somenus began to imprison anyone who would not submit to his new rule. They said Urbis killed the entire royal family."

DEZMUND: "Urbis—*Orion's bow*? That's impossible. It was destroyed along with Orion."

JOEL: "Whatever the case, I cannot help you anymore, Dezmund. I am done doing your dirty work; you will have to go find a new hero to kill your new king."

DEZMUND: "But we need to *stop* him—he is making himself a god, setting up temples and demanding worship. His power over the minds of men will be limitless and this world we have fought so hard to keep pure will die. He claims to have answered *the question*."

JOEL: "The fae always wanted a king who would take charge over the mortals, and answer their question. Everyone is getting what they want; why interfere?"

DEZMUND: "How can you be so stone-hearted? *Please*, Timbre Wulf, I need your help! We need to raise up an army, break through the gates and retake Arelle. Let's reclaim Urbis for ourselves and send Somenus back to Hades for *good!*"

JOEL: "If you want an army, then it is not with me that you should be pleading, it is the kings of men. Go, take the elf with you and make *him* your ambassador. He is idle enough to do anything. But I want no more fae coming here and trying to rope my family into your mess; I have already lost a son to you lot."

"Hanz?" Isabella gasped.

"Who is Hanz?"

"My brother. What's he saying about him?"

"Where's your brother?"

Isabella looked down. "He ran away a year ago—I don't know why. Has he heard from him? What's he *saying?*"

"He says he is done losing family members."

"Don't just *paraphrase!*"

THE CONVERSATION
────────── Between ──────────
JOEL and DEZMUND

DEZMUND: "Are you no longer *the Friend of the Fae?*"

JOEL: "I am your friend, Dezmund, but I am done risking my own life and my family's lives just to kill for the fae. I lost my wife to their hidden wars, must I lose my daughter as well? If my son wants to leave my house and try to live out a dead legacy of mine, that's *his* choice. I last saw him in town a week ago, if you wanted to find him, but he is not interested in warfare."

DEZMUND: "I am sorry to hear that, Timbre Wulf. I thought providence had dropped me into your hands, but perhaps not. If your son wants nothing to do with warfare, I won't waste my time with him: I'll take the elf."

JOEL: "How many of rhe fae have escaped Somenus' hunters? I imagine that if Korbin caught you, he's caught many."

Isabella broke away from Clover in a sudden burst of energy.

"Hanz is as close as *town*? And Papa concealed this from me?" Isabella barreled down towards the wood shed on the other side of the homestead and Clover hurried after her.

"You didn't know where he was?"

"I had no idea! Papa made it sound like he just disappeared," she shook her head in disbelief. "I can't believe he *lied* to me!"

"Where are you going? Don't you want to hear the rest of their conversation?" Clover threw his one last bargaining chip at her.

"I've heard enough." She pulled a cloak and a lantern stick from the shed.

Clover moved to block her path. "Where are you going?"

"Hanz is in town, and I'm going to find him!"

"*Now?*" Clover looked around, waiting for her father to pop out of a bush.

"My father, for once, is distracted; now is the time."

"It's dangerous, I had better come with you. You'll need a strong man to—"

Isabella turned slowly away. "Yeah, I don't think so."

"You can't stop me."

"But Clover, you're my distraction! I need you to stall him so I have enough time to get away! I *need* you!"

"I could *help* you—"

"Clover, if you really loved me, you would help me escape."

155

"Don't be ridiculous, of *course* I love you!" He huffed.

"Plus," Isabella pointed over at her sheep that wandered freely around the valley. "I need someone to keep watch over my flock!"

Clover's countenance dropped. "You're joking."

"I can't leave them unattended!"

"Isabella," Clover knelt down and took her hand. "Of course, your concern for your flock makes you more of a goddess than ever, but you can't expect me to just sit here waiting for you to return while watching *sheep!*"

"If you loved me, you wouldn't let them out of your sight; you would do what I asked, not what's *easy* for you. Promise me."

Clover dropped his head and reluctantly mumbled, "I promise: go."

Isabella thrust her arms around him and gave him a genuine embrace of gratitude. "Thank you, this means everything to me! Now remember: distract my father—tell him I went looking for a lost sheep, and he won't wonder where I have gone until tomorrow."

As Isabella turned to run off, Clover stopped her by the arm. "Isabella—come back to me. Remember: I love you."

Isabella paused. "Good bye, Clover." And at that, she disappeared into the night. Clover watched her leave, listening to her movements until she was no longer in earshot. Then he turned and stared blankly at the cluster of sheep that were returning his gaze.

"This should be interesting."

A FEW HOURS PASSED before Joel emerged from the homestead and came to find Clover napping in the grass. He woke the elf with generous kick to the stomach.

"Where is she?"

"Lost a sheep."

"You think I am a *fool?*" Joel roared, as he lifted Clover from the ground by the neck, once more, effortlessly.

"No!" Clover yelped. Knowing now that this was the legendary Timbre Wulf, Clover was stupefied.

"You listened in, *didn't* you? You confounded elf!"

"Of *course* I did!"

"Did you tell her anything?" His voice grew even louder.

"Everything."

"Damn!" Joel dropped Clover to the ground. "You *imbecile!*"

"Don't get mad at me; she's old enough to think for herself."

"Don't start!" He threw the mysterious bag back at Clover. "Now you listen to me: you are going to get off my property and help get this faerie where he needs to go."

"You can't tell me what to do."

Joel took him by the throat once more.

"Fine, fine—but I can't leave until Isabella comes back!" Clover shook him off.

"You'll leave right *now*!" he bellowed.

"I promised her I wouldn't leave the sheep!" Clover gasped in all sincerity.

The two men paused, both panting loudly, and looked at the group of ovis, which seemed to be watching Clover in anticipation.

"You, what?" Joel stammered.

"I promised her I wouldn't leave the sheep."

"You're not staying here." Joel crossed his arms.

"Would you have me break a promise?" Clover narrowed his eyes. Both paused in another moment of quiet.

"Fine, take the sheep—they're worthless to me without my daughter."

"But..."

Joel stepped closer with a roar, "Take the blasted sheep and get Dezmund where he wants to go!"

"But I told her I—"

Joel lowered his voice to barely a whisper. "If you ever want to see my daughter again, you help that faerie; do you understand?"

"Yes, sir."

Joel sighed and turned his back to Clover, feeling the weight of his daughter's departure.

"Take him back through the tunnel. There is a passage west through the mountains towards the Fero Plains. Speak to the Fero Lord; he may have the army Dezmund is looking for. Don't return until you have helped this fae kill the Faerie King. As for me, I need to find my daughter and clean up this mess."

Clover grabbed the sack reluctantly and tucked it into his belt. He didn't really care about the faerie's plight. Before today, he had never really cared about *anything*. However, nothing was going to stop him from getting back to Isabella: even if it meant he had to kill the Faerie King himself.

163

THERE IS, perhaps, nothing better for a young man than an impossible task. He has finally received a charge by which he could prove himself to the world—a world that disbelieves anything extraordinary could come from him. He may now set aside his formerly idle hours and use every ounce of strength he has to complete this charge.

Whether completing the task proves that he was remarkable all along, or if it changes him for the better, thereby making him remarkable, I cannot say. However, an impossible task itself tends to be the making of a man, whether he fails in it or not.

I am not sure if Clover realized at the time that his quest was thrown upon him with very little expectation that he would succeed, but it did not matter. This impossible task was exactly what he had been waiting for and, in his mind, the prize was well worth the trouble.

At last, he could prove himself—to himself.

CHAPTER III

In which

I Found My Master

EARTH: THE SPHERICAL WORLD twisting round and round, trapped in an endless, cyclical rhythm of day and night, life and death, good and evil. I grew up stuck in this cycle, not knowing that every day I was born into a new life and every night I died. Every day I had to remember who I was and what I was supposed to do; every night I would surrender to my heavy eyes and enter the spirit world inside my head.

I would have kept going on in this cycle of life and death forever if I had not been abruptly interrupted like a record part-way through a song. I got to see outside the cycle: I was shown what my world looked like from the outside.

The men and women of the Earth search for meaning beyond the cycle. Stuck with their feet firmly planted on the soil, they are unable to reach past their physical plane. However, a few of them, blessed beyond belief, are touched and lifted up by the *Watcher*: the only one left on Raqia who still knows how to look.

One of these blessed humans was me, Leonard Levi. Like the man in the Flammarion Engraving, I got to look through the firmament and beyond at the wonders that mortals long to see.

EARTH

Oxford

Tasmania

AEROSPACE
EARTH

We were on our way to see Benji, or so we thought. While we believed he was studying for his PhD at Oxford, in reality he had been traveling the globe for the last two years.

BENJI: MY BEST FRIEND. We grew up together like brothers. I knew I wasn't *cool* enough to be his close companion, but it was all the more special that he didn't care about that kind of thing. After the early death of Benji's parents, I was the family he needed. We grew into men together and encouraged one another in our passions. I encouraged him in his love of philosophy and he spurred me on with my writing. He believed in me when no one else did. I often wonder if that was due more to his love for me than any skill of mine. He made me feel like I could do anything I wanted!

It was a sad but beautiful day when I said good-bye to him at the airport. He was going off to Oxford to learn wisdom, and Lydia and I both knew he was going to make something of himself. We saw him as he truly was: a pure, gifted man with all the ambition and curiosity in the world. He was going to go far.

LYDIA: BENJI'S SISTER and my first love. She looked up to Benji even more than I, if that were possible. At the time, I truly believed that if perfection were possible, it would look like her. She was perfect innocence and purity to me. She had Benji's good looks but none of the grandeur, and her heart was like a source spring of mountain water: nature untouched by any evil effects of Death. She was, as I said, my first love.

You can imagine how thrilled I was when she asked me to come with her on a surprise visit to Oxford. We both missed Benji and he did a terrible job keeping in contact with anyone who wasn't physically near him. We loved that Benji was always a very present person, but when he left it was like we didn't exist. After three years of him being in school, we decided to show him our support by visiting him at Oxford.

OXFORD
ENGLAND

Our exciting trip to England turned into a nightmare when we couldn't find Benji. His roommate—who hadn't seen him in nearly *two years*—told us he dropped out to hike the Alps and was surprised we didn't know about it.

We followed leads through the Alps, which led us to Hungary, which led us to Ukraine, which led us into Siberia, where we found he had gone to India. As we went thousands and thousands of dollars into debt, we followed his trail from India to Singapore, Singapore to Australia, and Australia to Tasmania.

SINGAPORE

It is still a wonder that Lydia never fell for me after all that time. The two of us—alone and traveling the world for five months, staying in hostels, huts, and tents—became good friends, but never lovers. It was like she couldn't see past me as her brother, and I see now it was better that way. For all that time, she was without her brother Benji, but I was there.

The day we found Benji was like the day Henry Morton Stanley found David Livingston in the depth of Africa. It was surreal. It had been like chasing the ghost of our long-lost brother, and there he was: sitting by a campfire, looking up at us, and smiling.

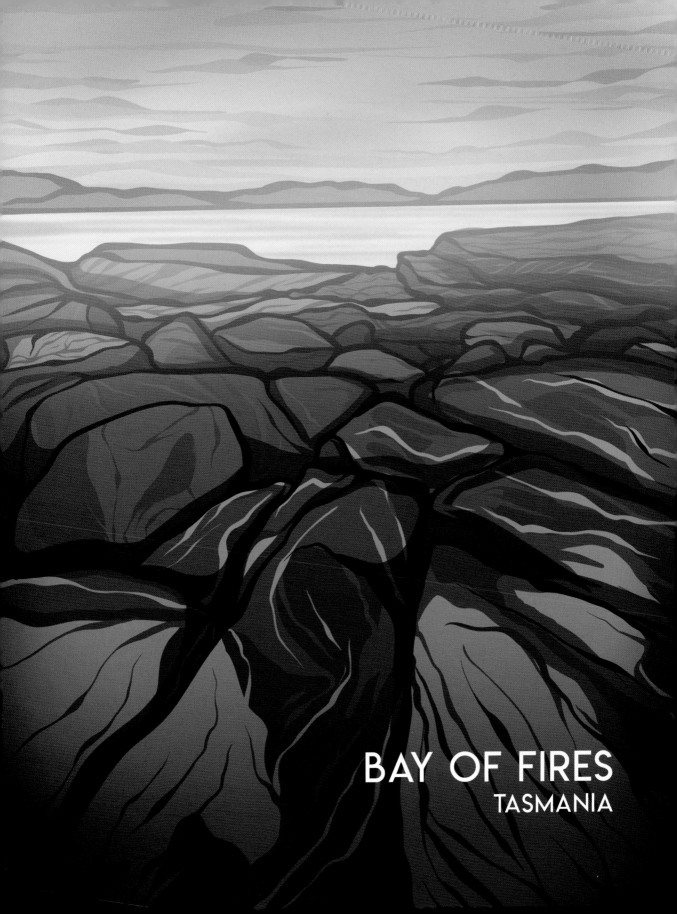

BAY OF FIRES
TASMANIA

Lydia and I weren't sure how to react. Exhausted, bewildered, and jostled by the joyous Benji, we attempted to greet him cheerfully.

"Come, sit by the fire; warm yourselves!"

We walked over to the crackling fire and seated ourselves, exchanging concerned looks. He didn't even *look* like Benji.

"What do you think of my home?" Benji gestured to his small campsite made up of a hand-made tent and a small fire. Lydia gawked at a couple of mangled-looking raw fish lying beside the fire.

"Benji—" she stammered.

"I have so much to tell you guys about all my travels! Here, *eat;* you must be hungry!" Benji pulled some dried fish from a crumbled up wad of brown paper. I felt Lydia lean closer to me and grab my arm as if Benji's offer frightened her in some way.

"Yeah, about these—*travels*, Benji," I took the fish he offered, "didn't you know we thought you were still in Oxford?"

"What? No—*really*? God! Didn't I leave a note?"

"A *note*?" Lydia stammered and I felt her grip tighten.

"Come on, Benji, a note? This isn't the Dark Ages; you could have called, emailed—you left us *nothing!*" The frustration of my months-long chase began to surface.

Benji scoffed in annoyance. "I am sorry that my escape was hard for you to understand, but I'm sure that this journey was a good thing for you; it led you *here!*"

"Benji," Lydia spoke up quietly, "we thought you might have died! Or that we would never see you again!"

"Yeah, Benj. This journey was not the funnest thing for us. I'm kind of in a lot of debt, and I definitely lost my job!"

"Set yourself free from that way of thinking, Leo. You can only really experience life when you are free from the man-trap of the Western world!"

"Benji, you're talking like we know what you mean, but we don't. You used to believe, like we do, that a beautiful life can be lived anywhere: even in the West." Lydia's voice grew stronger.

"What got into you, Benji? What escape are you talking about?" I watched him carefully.

"*This.*" Benji held up a small, tattered book with the name *Rasselas* scratched across the front of it. Benji grinned. "This book changed my life."

Lydia and I exchanged unimpressed glances.

Benji leaned back with a sigh, gazing lovingly at his book. "I began reading this at Oxford and I didn't even get through the second chapter before I knew it was about me. *I* am Rasselas!"

"Who?" I scratched my head, mustering patience.

Benji grunted, annoyed. "Do you know Samuel Johnson?"

"Sam, from our fourth-grade math class?" I reached.

"No, Leo." Benji sighed loudly. "Samuel Johnson, the literary genius!"

"Oh, uh, no. I don't, sorry."

"He wrote this book on a whim to pay for his mother's funeral. He sought to answer the question: why are the poor happier than the rich?"

"Are they? Huh."

"This character—Rasselas, the Prince of all that's beautiful, never seeing any death or sorrow, kept from all ugliness and sin— grows tired of his life. He is a prince with everything and yet *nothing*. No happiness."

"How are *you* Rasselas?" Lydia piped up.

Benji continued, caught in the excitement of his own tale. "I was just sitting there in my beautiful dormitory, in a comfortable chair, sun shining in through the window, on the grounds of the most prestigious school in the world, enjoying a glass of expensive wine, reading this book—and it hit me: I feel what he feels. Listen to this!" He cracked open his book to a well-marked spot and read aloud:

> *I fancy that I should be happy if I had something to pursue, but possessing all that I could want, I find one day and one hour exactly like another except that the latter is still more tedious than the former.*

"I looked around me and felt the same distaste. I was pursuing wisdom while surrounded by pleasure, ease and comfort. And here:

> *I shall long to see the miseries of the world, since the sight of them is necessary to happiness.*

"And it hit me: I am getting a two-dimensional picture of the world if all I do is study it from my spoiled perspective of comfort and ease. How can I really know wisdom if I know not sorrow? Think about Tasmania: this place is beautiful, but it is also a tragedy. When Westerners discovered this place, they wiped out every last native before moving onto the island, sparing none. How can I enjoy the pleasures of this life without also knowing evil and suffering?"

"What happened with Rasselas?" asked Lydia.

"He escaped his heavenly prison and went out into the chaotic world, searching for the best life to live. So that's what *I* did!" Benji's eyes widened with excitement. "I left everything for the true pursuit of knowledge! I took only what I could carry on my back, and I went searching, as he did, for my *choice of life!* I need to know what I am supposed to *do* in this life."

"And what happened to him in the end? Did he find his *choice of life*?" I asked.

Benji chuckled. "I confess, I have not yet finished it."

"A book that small? You don't even want to know how it *ends*?" I shook my head. Oh, Benji—he never really finished books.

"I make my own end! I must find *my* choice of life!"

Lydia and I looked at each other again, both feeling equally unsettled.

"Have you found it?" I asked him.

Benji answered excitedly. "You wouldn't *believe* the things I have seen and experienced! I have lived amongst the most fascinating people and cultures. I have seen both the beauty of sorrow and the pain of pleasure. I have felt things, seen things, saved lives, laughed and cried, gathered and burned, I have loved and hated—I have experienced so much!"

"So why are you still searching? You look, to me, more lost than ever," said Lydia.

Benji glanced over with annoyance at his sister. "And you think you know what it means to look lost? Look at *yourself:* doing nothing with your life and waiting for someone else to give you purpose? You've been lost your whole life. I, at least, have gone searching for answers. You've been content with just doing *nothing*."

"Hey—not cool! What's gotten into you, Benji? This is *Lydia!*" I interjected.

"Maybe I have had enough exposure to have the boldness to speak as I find," Benji shrugged. "She needs to hear it."

Lydia, with tears welling, restrained her anger and answered, "You are right, Benji. I *have* been content, which is something I have never seen in you. While you were searching the whole world for answers, I remained in the same place: content. Fault me if it makes you feel better about your life choices, but I am unmoved."

Benji snarled and clenched his fists. "You're too scared to do anything else—you hide behind your sewing and homemaking skills."

"I haven't *wanted* to do anything else! At least I have *made* a choice, but you are determined to taste everything before you choose which plate to eat from."

Benji stood and thrust his finger toward the darkening sky. "I chose the pursuit of *wisdom!* Is there *anything* greater than that?"

Lydia turned away from him and hid her face in her hands.

"Come on, Benji." I stood, blocking Benji's view of Lydia. "We came here 'cause we were worried about you! Lydia has been all alone back home with no Benji and nothing but her sewing to support herself. After all you've been through, have you lost your compassion?"

Benji sighed once more and shook his head. "Look, I'm sorry—I wasn't expecting to see you guys. I just *knew* you wouldn't understand me."

I stepped closer to my friend, reaching out a hand. "We are *trying* to understand you, Benji. We came all this way!"

Benji recoiled and turned his back to me. "I just need some space. Help yourself to the food." He stormed off and disappeared into the rocks. I can only imagine he was as disappointed as we were by the interaction.

I looked back at Lydia who was softly sobbing into her hands. During this whole trip, littered with disappointments, I had never seen her cry until now. I went to her side and sat where Benji had been, took her hands, and made her look at me.

"Hey, its ok; we found him! This is what we have been waiting for!" I smiled reassuringly.

"I know. I should be happy," she sniffed. "I just feel like I don't even know him anymore."

"Benji has always been a wanderer, this shouldn't shock us too much. He just needs us to meet him where he is at."

"But he's like a ship with no anchor and no port, just tossing around on the waves: aimless."

"He's trying to find a port, Lydia, in his way. Let's try and understand him."

Lydia dropped her face back into her hands with a sob. I just held her.

"It's like he didn't even miss me. Like he's not even happy to see me," she sniffed.

"Hey—it's going to be ok. Of *course* he missed you! We all are

confused about how to do this, let's just—"

I tried to keep talking, but my mouth seemed to stop working. Lydia suddenly looked up at me with a terrified expression. Both she and I were stunned by what we saw. What appeared to be blue, electric lights encircled us.

I saw her mouth out my name as the lights covered every inch of our bodies, and then—from what I know now—*we disappeared.*

WILDERNESS

My head was spinning and my body experienced the delayed movements akin to the feeling of drunkeness. Sensing soft grass between my fingers, I opened my eyes to see that I was lying flat on my back in the middle of a dense wood. The first thing my eyes saw was a silhouette standing over me, shrouded in glowing light from a daytime sky.

The figure raised his hands high above its head, and for a moment, I thought he was going to kill me! I threw my arms over my face and clenched my eyes closed.

"Welcome! My long-lost apprentice!" The voice of the figure cried over me.

"What the *crap?*" I uncovered my head and tried to sit up.

The mysterious man continued. "Oh, how long I have waited and watched you! Since our devastating separation when you were an infant, I have long awaited the day where we could once again be reunited!"

"You *have?*" I stared in surprise, drunkenly accepting everything I saw.

"Oh, my boy, the gifts bestowed on you as an infant by the fae were only the beginning of the rich blessing I will lavish on you as I take you on the journey of a lifetime! You have searched for meaning, all the while not knowing it was *I* who had it to give to you! You are my mortal and I am your immortality!" he declared loudly.

"Immortality?"

"Your father tried to keep us apart, and I kept my promise to stay away while you were a child. But now that you have grown, I am free to come and bring you to the world I have prepared for you for *generations!"*

"A world? Wait—my *dad?"* I stood up, dusted myself off, and surveyed my summoner, still too dazed to react properly.

"Forget your old life, my boy, for your true future now awaits you. Oh my child—we now have eternity to find out *just* how important you are!"

"Wow! Man—that's crazy, thanks!" I laughed. "I just wish I knew what your were talking about. Um, where's Lydia?"

I nodded heartily at the man, wanting him to feel like I was listening, and looked around for Lydia. Though still in a semi-drunken state, I knew that whatever happened to me must have happened to her too. I was sure she was nearby.

"Ah yes, your sister. Well, sometimes the transport can be a bit hard to control when I'm bringing over multiple people. She's around here somewhere, and possibly your other, uh, *friend*." The man looked around and scratched his head.

"My sister..." I stared at him.

"Never mind her, Benjamin! *You* are the one I have planned this life for, and we will travel this world together!"

"For years you have searched for wisdom beyond your understanding and for places not yet discovered! I bring you now to my child-world, and together we will discover new journeys and experiences that your sun and moon know nothing about!"

"Yeah, um, Benji's not here, he—" I swayed nervously.

He stopped short, "what was that?" He narrowed his eyes. "Good God, who are *you*?"

I smiled politely and shrugged. "Yeah, uh, sorry to have to disappoint, but I'm not Benji! I'm, uh—Leo! The... *friend?*"

He didn't look impressed. "I *specifically* targeted Benji," he moaned, more to himself than to me.

I shrugged. "People move around. You using some kind of portal or something?"

"Oh stop trying to act like you know anything about what's happening! You're an unfortunate bystander who got mixed up in my surprise for *Benjamin*." He grumbled and pulled out a pocket watch to check the time.

This was my first encounter with Momentum. Yes, his current name is Momentum. I still feel a little bad that I spoiled his meeting with his beloved adoptee *(or kidnapee—more on that later)*. But honestly, it was better this way. He may have been just as disappointed by his reunion with Benji as I was with mine.

"Sounds good! Happy to be involved. So, should we go back to—*wherever*—and get him?"

"I'm surprised you're not more jarred by this miraculous encounter," he looked up from his watch at me suspiciously.

"Oh, I'm a writer! I think this is great!"

He rolled his eyes. "You watch too much TV; it's de-mystifying your generation."

"For sure! Wow, thats *good*." I pulled out my quote book.

"Yes, well," he shrugged modestly, "I do say some pretty profound things."

"So are you saying that we are over-stimulated with so many ideas and information that we are no longer impressed with true miracles when we witness them?"

"Yes, I guess so," he eyed me curiously. "Anyway, I really anticipated a different kind of reaction when I brought you here."

"Oh, well I'm not Benji; he will give you a *great* reaction! He's like this awesome, curious truth-seeker who just loves new places and ideas!" I reassured him.

"Hmm, perhaps you're right. I *have* been anticipating Benjamin. Either that, or you're still reeling from the cosmic travel."

"Exactly!" I pointed my pencil at him. "So, should we, like, go get him or whatever-it-is you do?"

He frustratedly scratched his head. "You make it sound so easy. It took a lot of power to bring you from one world to another while I was on neither."

"Wow, sounds pretty cool!"

"Yes, well, I'll need to head back to the source if we are going to get Benjamin."

"What about Lydia? Didn't you say she's somewhere around here? We should probably find her!"

"Oh, calm down. This will only take a minute, and then Benjamin and I can find her together. I am not going to do any adventuring without him! *Come on!*"

Momentum grabbed me by the wrist and punched a button on the side of his watch.

THIS, FRIENDS, was my SECOND time through what I have come to call the *"Flammarion Tunnel."* The first time—when Momentum unexpectedly dragged us from Earth—was such a shock that we were unconscious for the journey. This time however, I was aware enough to experience the trip through the barriers of the firmament and beyond. The trip felt both instant and eternal as I swirled, weightless, through a colourful tunnel of stars.

I felt us moving higher and higher, passing the emptiness of space and continuing on into the divine realms. I knew so little at the time of what was happening, and so I just gazed in wonder and awe.

I don't know how to describe what I felt as we passed between the barriers. It was as if my life was no longer spread across years of time, but was all-existing in one single moment. I was young and old, mature and innocent, dead and alive, all at the same time. All of me existed at once in that journey; I felt both love for people I didn't yet know and sadness for things I hadn't yet experienced. My spirit was awake in full.

How can I draw that? I can't. We cannot draw it. Sorry

COSMOS CHAMBER

RAQIA

Once we reached the other side, we were both standing inside a dimly-lit chamber. I wish I could remember it better. At the time, I didn't know how precious or how old that place was. Instead, I just stared at Momentum as he shuffled around the room looking for who-knows-what.

The chamber was shaped like a half-sphere. The floor was made of a perfectly smooth marble interlaid with what looked like streams of blue crystal, and the arced ceiling was covered in an intricate mosaic design and—for the life of me—I wish I had looked longer. (In recent years, Momentum has designed a replica of the dome in his fortress, but he is always telling me that it doesn't hold a candle to the original). All I really remember of the ceiling above me were depictions of stars, clouds, water, and winged figures.

At the center of the chamber was a square table with a map painted on its surface. Behind me, I saw the portal from which we had just emerged. The portal, called the Lapis Gate, was against one of the chamber walls. Framed with lead and coloured glass, this glowing blue gate looked like a vertical wall of still water.

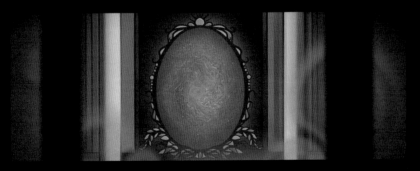

"Wow." I reached out my hand to the portal only for it to get slapped away by Momentum.

"Don't *touch* anything!" He yelled as he fiddled with his watch again. "*Damn*, I can't find him!"

I was about to offer help, but figured he wanted me out of the way. There was a slight rumbling under my feet. I looked at my guide, expecting an explanation. He didn't seem to notice so I walked across the chamber towards the source of the noise, which seemed to be coming from the other side of the wall.

"Uh…" I tried to get his attention as I placed my ear against the wall. The rumbling I heard through the wall sounded like pounding from the other side which grew increasingly louder.

"*Get away from that wall!*" Momentum screamed. He tackled me just in time as the wall exploded into a shower of rocks and mortar.

All I could hear were ringing and muffled voices as I lay on the marble, covered in debris. I pushed myself up to my feet and coughed violently, groping for a wall to lean on, then fell back down. Momentum lay next to me, and appeared to yell but I couldn't make out what he said.

Someone was emerging from a cloud of smoke and ashes from the opening in the wall. I wiped my eyes and shook my head; my ears began to clear and I could hear muffled words.

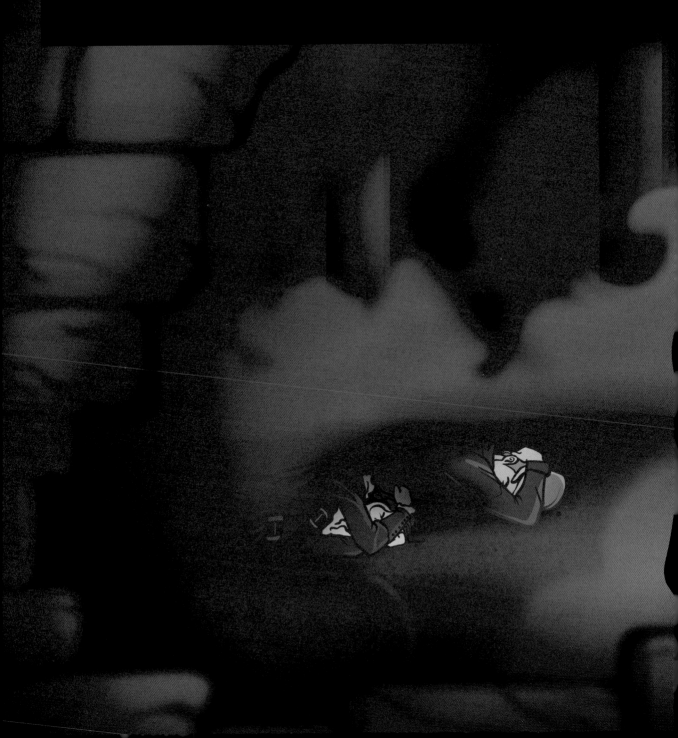

"Look at me, Momentum." The intruder called with a soft but eerie voice. I saw now that Momentum was shielding his eyes from the figure.

"*Damn you!* Damn you back to where you belong!" roared my protector.

My heart began to pound as shadows reached out from the figure to surround the chamber. They crept closer and closer to us.

"You *will* show your allegiance," said the voice. "Move away from the gate." I rose to my feet and my body felt chilled to the core.

"*Never!*" cried Momentum as he pushed me backwards into the portal. As I fell into the tunnel once more, Momentum leaped in after me, followed by a dark, gloved hand reaching in after him. In the same moment, Momentum crushed the face of his watch, causing an explosion of fire to burst from the source of the portal and follow us all through the Flammarion Tunnel. We traveled downwards until we plummeted back into the clearing where I had first found Momentum.

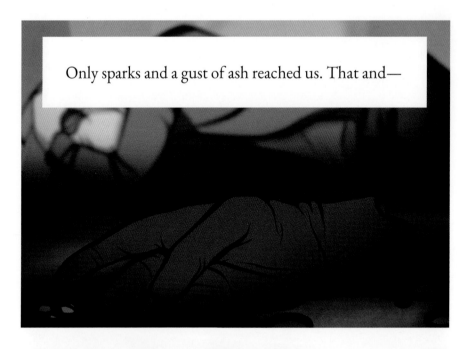

Only sparks and a gust of ash reached us. That and—

"AUGH!"

I screamed and hurriedly backed away from the severed but bloodless hand laying in the grass. "What the heck!"

Curling myself into the fetal position, I trembled violently, finally having a realistic reaction to these experiences.

Momentum, also lying in the grass, stared at the hand without a change of expression. He looked at his broken watch, sighed, and tucked it in his pocket. "*Damn*," he cursed under his breath.

I had a lot of questions, but struggled to find a voice. My body wouldn't let me do or say anything, insisting on being in shock. We both lay motionless and silent, I'm not sure for how long.

"So many things," Momentum mumbled at length, "so many things lost today."

"Yeah," I said, surprised that my response came out verbally. "Me too."

Momentum shifted in the grass and let out a very long, deep breath. "Damn."

I didn't really understand what it was that he lost, but I tried to comfort him. "Sorry that I wasn't Benji."

My companion huffed. "It doesn't matter now."

"What was your connection with him?" I stretched my arms, which were numb and cold, turned to lay on my side, keeping the creepy severed hand out of sight.

"It was something you wouldn't understand."

"Ok." I shrugged.

Momentum sighed loudly. "I knew him as a baby. We... he..."

"You had," I tried to guess, "plans for him?"

"Yeah, you could say that."

"What kind of plans?"

I now know that Momentum wouldn't usually entertain private questions from a nobody like me. I think I was just in the right place at the right time.

"I had hopes for him to be my..." he paused and looked at me, "*apprentice.*"

"What did you want to teach him?"

"Everything."

I paused and thought for a moment. "Can't you still?"

Momentum stared at me with a disappointed look on his face. "Don't you realize?" He clearly didn't want to deliver the bad news.

"I don't really know much of what is going on—at all." I smiled.

"I guess not." He closed his eyes and lay back down. "We are stuck here: *forever*."

I didn't say anything, laying back also.

I really didn't know what to feel. He just told me a fact that obviously changed my life, but it didn't feel like it. *Forever?* I didn't even know where I was!

"Wait!" I sat up suddenly and looked over at Momentum. "What about *Lydia*?"

"She'll be around here somewhere," said he, with his arm over his eyes.

I sighed in relief. At least I hadn't abandoned her in the middle of Tasmania!

"What about Benji?"

"I don't know, kid—still on Earth."

I stood and looked around the thick wood.

"You know, my name is Leo; you can call me Leo." I offered. He didn't respond. "What's your name?"

He groaned. "Momentum," he said reluctantly. "You may call me 'sir'."

"Yes, sir." I smiled. "And uh, what is *that?*" I pointed at the severed hand. Momentum lifted his arm from his eyes and looked over at the thing.

"A ghost." I saw him shudder. "At least I—" he sat up and looked at me, "—well, I will have to be content with what I was able to do. I guess we should probably find your sister."

I was about to correct him, but instead I smiled and nodded. Benji was gone, and though she didn't know it, Lydia needed a brother if she was to be stuck forever in—

"Wait!" I slapped my forehead. "Where the heck *are* we?"

Momentum looked at me with a hint of joy in his face and said, "Paidion."

—

It was a new beginning for me, standing there next to this total stranger who had pulled me away from everything I knew. One may expect me to be much more upset than I was in that moment, but instead I had this profoundly strange feeling.

219

SOMETHING had opened up in my mind. It must have been dormant for my whole life until this day—an awakening of enlightenment. After passing through the Flammarion Tunnel, something new was born in my mind and heart. I didn't yet comprehend it all, but something about me was different. It felt like my eyes saw new colours; my ears heard fresh sounds; my body experienced heightened awareness to every sense of touch; and my heart—oh my heart—felt deep, undying love. My innermost soul was awake.

The culmination of all these things resulted in one, definitive feeling: excitement. A part of my soul that had been dead was suddenly alive, and I knew that the rest of my life—my *real* life—was stretched out before me.

At this time, I was like an infant that had come into its world, dazzled by the light and in awe of its new surroundings. I didn't know why I was awake, or what it meant, but I would soon begin to walk a new path that would lead me to something that I didn't think I would ever have any conviction or clarity about: my *purpose*.

Read on, friends, read on. Read on as I take you deep into the Tempest that sucked me away from my clockwork cycle of death and into my chaotic storm of purpose. Stoke your hunger for the meaning behind the physical; fall in love, as I did, with the fathomless sovereignty of the great Tempest which—if we let it—crashes us upon new soils that we never could have found on our own.

To Be Continued In

TEMPEST

Volume Two

Nothing there could harness me.

Floating aimless, free and lost;
Freedom with a dreadful cost.

Caught into a coiling net;
A sovereign Tempest I had met.

My will a jest, my hopes were null;
Playing with a raging bull.

My frozen hands released the mast,
And then the Tempest reigned at last.

GLOSSARY

Ancient Scrypt: The ancient language written and spoken originally by the native inhabitants of Paidion.

Arelle *(the "Fair City")*: the heart of the Faerie Kingdom. It is a city with beauty beyond imagination, heavily walled and protected, where mortals can only dream to enter.

Coastal Elves: The small colony of elves whose kingdom, Celestia, resides on the Blue Coast on the southeast coast of Raqia.

Cosmos, the: The order and purpose of the universe when seen in its whole. The Seven Layers of the Cosmos are: the Heavens, the Waters Above, Raqia, Space, the Lowlands, the Waters Below, and the Underworld.

Cosmos Chamber: The lost, ancient chamber of the original Faerex Council where the Lapis Gate was hidden for thousands of years.

Death: the ruler of the Lowlands, the Waters Below, and Hades.

Death Curse, the: An ancient curse that placed the Lowlands under the rulership of Death. Due to this curse, Lowland dwellers earned the title of "mortals."

Dyewatre Inn: A small inn outside the borders of the Southe. The waters run a deep blue due to the dye houses upstream.

Elme: The city and home of the Woodland Elves that sits just on the outskirts of the Raqian Woodlands. Home to Clover.

Elves: A mortal race that was a result of humans and faeries intermarrying in ancient times. Though they can live for hundreds, or even thousands of years, they are still slowly affected by the Death Curse.

Exsilium Prisons *(Exile Bags)*: These are magikal bags created by the King of the Faeries. They are able to ensnare any fae—making them small—and removing their ability to channel magik into an item.

Faeries *(Fae, Watchers)*: the immortal native race of Raqia. These winged beings are both physical and spirit beings, meaning they can manifest their appearance in different ways at will. The fae's lifesource is centered around magik, which is a mystical power emanating from all things in the physical world. There can only be one thousand fae in existence at a time.

Faerex: The title for the King of the Fae, who reigns from Arelle. He has sovereign power over all the land of Raqia, though not necessarily all of the governments.

Fero Lands: Home to the Fero people. This large colony of humans is known in Raqia to be some of its newest dwellers, as they have only been dwelling there for nearly one thousand years.

Firmament: A hard, unsurpassable barrier that separates the Lowlands from the Heavens. It is a transparent, hard shell that holds up the glassy sea, making it impossible to enter the Heavens.

Flammarion Tunnel: The passage between the fabrics of reality, which can in an eternal instant transport one from place to place, time to time and world to world. It is the only way one may travel from the Lowlands to Raqia.

Friend of the Fae: This is an extremely rare honorary title given to any mortal who is so loved by a faerie that they receive the gift of immortality. This gift is in effect as long as the bestowing fae remains alive. This title was first given to Timbre Wulf.

Heavens, the: Home to the the true source of light, emanating from the Creator. Dwelling there are visions too wonderful for me to ever know or describe. In the ancient Hebrew creation account, Light, Day and Night existed before the creation of the Sun and Moon. The true light and the passing of time poured out of Heaven, and this, I have been told, is what governs the days and nights on the table world of Raqia.

The word "Heavens," in the ancient Hebrew Bible, is not *Plural*, but *Dual*, signifying that there are two Heavens. There is the Heaven where the Divine Spirits are able to dwell and may enter the presence of the Creator, and then there is the Highest Heaven, where the throne sits above all other creation.

Imperium: A fae's magikal item through which they store and use their magikal abilities and authority. A fae can store limited magik inside their bodies, and so they choose an item of great sentimental value and store their power inside.

Kronosians: An order of monks in Paidion who follow the teachings and traditions of St Kronos. St Kronos was a prophet who dwelled just outside the Southern Stomen borders and taught the people of Paidion new language, medicine and understanding to their scriptures around one thousand years prior to this story. The Kronosian Monks founded monasteries around Paidion as places for learning and sanctuary. The Kronosian Monks are celibates who pledge their lives to serve their God and bring sanctuary to others.

Lapis Gate, the: The first of the two Great Portals made by the original Faerie Council. Unlike the Crimson Gate, the light emanating from the magik portal is blue since the Lapis Gate was created from the waters of the Glassy Sea. This portal is able to open a gate anywhere and anytime, and can be remotely controlled by Momentum's Imperium.

Lowlands, the *(Earth, Paidion and the two other physical realms)*: The physical worlds under the firmament. Earth was the first of the Lowlands to be created out of the Sea. He was made out of water, and he is home to living mankind. Not long after his creation, Earth was cursed and has been ruled by Death since.

Three other Lowlands were created after the Earth, and one of these is called Paidion. I would say more if I knew more. The Lowlands are home to the ruler of the Element of Earth: the Aurochs.

Magik: A mystical power emanating from all things in the physical world.

Northe, the: The second of the two large Stomen kingdoms in Paidion. This autocracy is known for its antagonistic and warlike culture.

Orion: The first king of men on Raqia.

Paradise Valley: The home of Timbre Wulf, consisting of a 200 acre valley within a dome of razor-sharp mountains. There is only one way in or out, which can only be found either if you are not looking for it, or if you already know where it is.

Raqia: The faerie world that sits above the firmament. With its foundations resting down on the four Lowlands, it is a table-like world that is suspended above the stars and its top scratches the bottom of the Firmament.

Opposite to Earth, the Sun, Moon and Stars are beneath Raqia. Day and night are governed not by celestial bodies, but by the divine light emanating from the Heavens.

Raqian Woodlands: The labyrinthine forest that covers a vast space across the face of Raqia. This place of mystical happenings and mysterious dwellings is home to those who wish not to be known or discovered and is often a sanctuary to those in need of protection.

Salemn: The capital city of the Southe

Southe, the: The first of the two kingdoms of Stomen in Paidion. The Southe is governed by a carefully crafted rule of law and is far more religiously inclined than the Northe. The Southe was the first to follow the Kronosian order and realign their language and beliefs to follow it.

Stomen (From 'Stone Men'): The race of humans who dominate the majority of Paidion. The men of this race are born with a stone on the back of their necks. In the Southe, this stone is ceremonially removed at birth.

Space *(the Expanse)*: The Separation between the Heavens and the Lowlands. In this vast space, the Sun, Moon and Stars dwell. This emptiness is said to be home to the ruler of the Element of the Air: Ziz. Some say she lived in the Sun, and was able to die and rise along with it.

Timbre Wulf: A legendary human who was the first to receive the title *Friend of the Fae*. He was an armour-clad warrior, blessed by many fae, and wielding a immensely powerful staff called Beatus.

Tribes, the *(the Border Tribes)*: The micronations that are scattered across Paidion not consisting of Stomen.

Underworld, the *(Sheol, Hades)*: The world under the Sea, where the spirits of the dead dwell. It is not so much an evil place as a place of death—though the ruler of the Underworld, Death, is evil.

Egyptians named this place the Duat—where the sun god, Ra, would go to die when the sun set, and then would be reborn in a new day.

Ancient Mesopotamians called the underworld "the Great City," a fairly accurate description from what I know. The Underworld is supposedly home to the ancient beast known as the Dragon: the ruler of the Element of Fire.

Urbis: "*The builder and destroyer of cities*," the legendary bow belonging to Orion.

Waters Above, the *(The Glassy Sea)*: Above Raqia, at the very top of the physical realm, is a hard shell. This shell, the Firmament, resembles an unbreakable glass. The Firmament holds up the Waters Above—waters so pure that they bestow long life to anyone who drinks of them. Even humans live remarkably long lives on Raqia, as their seas find their source in the "The Fall of Life."

Many believe there to be an opening in the Firmament, from where the Glassy Sea pours gently down onto Raqia. This is called "The Fall of Life." None has ever seen this waterfall, but since the northwestern corners of my Master's Raqian maps are uncharted, I have often wondered if it is there.

Waters Below, the: The Sea. These waters were widely known in ancient times as the entrance to the Underworld. While we may think of the Sea as beautiful and tranquil, any ancients who ever tried to cross it only met death. In ancient narratives, anything that dwelt in or came out of the Sea brought death. Perhaps it was intuition that made sailors call the Sea a "she," for these waters were known to be produce life. They were female waters. This Sea represents pre-creation, for she gave birth to the Lowlands.

The Sea is also home to the ruler of the Element of Water, the Leviathan, who ushers the dead into the underworld and guards its gates.

Woodland Elves: A colony of elves that live on the borders of the Raqian Woodlands. They are solitary, pensive and skeptical—priding themselves in their intellect and knowledge of the spiritual realms. They are poets, musicians, philosophers, and gardeners who investigate the connections between nature and truth.

In Memory

of

Elsa Stewart